This is artist Frederick E. Fahdt's conception of the DYNA-SOAR boost-glide vehicle as it will be carried into space by the TITAN II intercontinental ballistic missile as a booster. Developed by The Martin Company and approved by the U. S. Air Force, the ultrasonic manned glider atop the booster is being developed by Boeing Company.

Other books by Lloyd Mallon

SPACE FLIGHT
A GUIDE TO ASTRONOMY

SPACE SCIENCE
BY LLOYD MALLAN

Titan, America's mightiest missile, is shown here as it accelerated to 5,000 mph at an altitude of about 30 miles above Cape Cañaveral. Final speed will be more than 15,000 mph. Special tracking camera with 500-in. f.1 lens made this amazing photo for technical study.

This photo as well as inset color photo on the cover are from the U.S. Air Force Ballistic Missile Division; large cover photo is Official USAF release from The Martin Co.

AMERICA'S MIGHTIEST MISSILE

LARRY EISINGER   •   EDITOR-IN-CHIEF

THE DO-IT-YOURSELF SERIES

arco publishing co. inc.

NEW YORK CITY 17, NEW YORK

Published 1961 by Arco Publishing Company, Inc.
480 Lexington Avenue, New York 17, N. Y.

Library of Congress Catalog Card Number: 61-13795

629.4

M29ᴅ

44209

Dec. 1962

ACKNOWLEDGEMENT

Without the fine cooperation of the following persons and organizations, this book could neither have been compiled nor written. The author's appreciation is beyond words. At Hq., Air Research and Development Command: Lt. General Bernard Schriever, Commander, and Major Ed Tarbutton; at Hq., Air Force Ballistic Missile Division: Maj. General Osmond Ritland, Commander, Lt. Colonel William McGinty, Director of the Office of Information, Major Tom Ellington, Chief of Public Information Division, Captain John Hinds, Deputy Chief, Public Information Division, Colonel Albert Wetzel, Director of the Titan ICBM Program, Captain William Dean, Deputy Director and Executive Officer and Lieutenant Howard Garrick, Administrative Officer, Titan Weapon System Program Office, Colonel Langdon Ayers, Director of Propulsion Development, Colonel Norman Murray, Head of Personnel Sub-system on Titan, Colonel Preston Newton, Director of 6594 Test Wing (Satellite), Colonel Roger Shannahan, Executive Officer, Atlas ICBM Program, Lt. Colonel Billy McCarrol, Chief of Convair Field Office to Atlas Program, Lt. Colonel Leyrer, Chief of Titan Configuration Control Division, Major Irv Newirth, Public Information Division, Major Harwell Boyd, Chief of Plans and Programs Division on Titan, Major Larry Walker, Assistant Director of Atlas Program, Major Vernard Webb, Assistant for Test Evaluation, 6594 Test Wing (Satellite), Captain John Barbato, Information Officer of 6565 Test Wing at Vandenberg AFB, Captain Richard Jay, Information Officer, 6594 Test Wing (Satellite), Captain Richard King, Public Information Division, Phil Booth, Head of the Still Photo Services Library of Aerospace Corp., Havey Roisman, Still Photo Editorial Associate, Aerospace, Dr. Alfred Rockefeller, Jr., AFBMD Historian, Elmer Franklin, Test Manager on Titan Program for Space Technology Laboratories, Ann Fratus, Secretary to the Director of Information; at the Ballistic Missile Center: Paul Frankfurt, Deputy Chief, Office of Information; at Wright Air Development Division: Carroll High, Acting Chief of Information, Robert Maltby, Deputy Chief of Information, George Sturgis, Information Specialist, Jack Tenholm, Executive Chief of DYNA-SOAR Systems Project Office; at USAF Hq., the Pentagon: Major James Sunderman, Head of Book Programs, Major Larry Tacker, Chief, Captain Bill Mack, Alice Adams Martin, Helen Burnart — all of the Magazine and Book Branch, Lt. Colonel Robert Wilson, Technical Liaison to Deputy Chief of Staff, Development; at Hq., Air Force Missile Test Center: Major Ken Grine, Chief of Information Services, Lieutenant Walter Ryland, Master Sergeant Ted Wassil and Staff Sergeant George Fleming; at the USAF New York Office of Information Services: Colonel "Chip" Woodruff and Major Ken McFarland, Chief and Deputy Chief respectively; at the U. S. Navy Magazine and Book Branch, the Pentagon: Commander Russell Buffkins, Chief, and Lt. Commander A. E. Atkinson; at the U. S. Army Office of the Chief of Ordnance Research, the Pentagon: Fred McHugh (ret.), Gordon Harris and Joe Penton; at Hq., the National Aeronautics and Space Administration: Joe Stein and Dick Mittauer; among the contractors cooperating were the Lockheed Missiles and Space Division, the Aircraft Nuclear Propulsion Department of General Electric and the various Divisions of The Martin Company. Special appreciation must be expressed for Ray Gill, Editor, and Bob Vatter, Artist-Designer, who suffered the birthpangs of this book every step of the way with the author. Particularly, I would like to thank A. Donald Brice, Director of Advertising and Publicity at the Dictaphone Corporation, for his usual fine cooperation: the authenticity of this book would have been diminished without the use of a miniaturized Dictet tape recorder for interviewing.

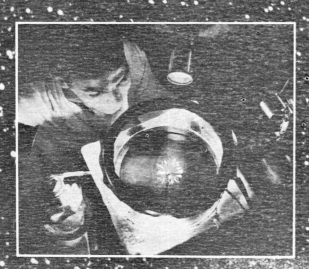

CONTENTS

With humility and gratitude, this book is dedicated to the Ballistic and Space Systems Division (formerly the Ballistic Missile Division) of the U. S. Air Force—whose hard-working, deeply sincere, farsighted personnel forms an organization that effectively creates and manages the development of America's most powerful instruments to deter war and stimulate peaceful scientific research. **L. M.**

Shown in this photo is the unloading of both stages of the mighty ICBM TITAN from the hold of a C-133 HERCULES propjet at Vandenburg Air Force Base, California, headquarters of the Pacific Missile Range.

Air Force Space Systems Division

INTRODUCTION

Since early 1958, almost exactly three years ago as of this writing, satellites and space probes of the United States have revolutionized the scientific thinking of mankind. These mere three years, among the millenia that civilization counts as recorded history, have revealed more information about the nature of the world we live on and the apparently empty space it hurtles through, than man has gathered for a thousand years—as he speculated and strived with puny, if ingenious, instruments to penetrate the dense curtain of the Earth's atmosphere to solve the mystery of his existence.

Things have been learned in these three years that will immeasurably benefit the whole human race, scientifically and physically. Yet mankind would never have acquired this new and revolutionary knowledge—if it had not been for remarkable developments in the weapon systems of war.

This book attempts to show the interconnections between a modern weapon system and its stimulation of pure scientific research. It also tries to emphasize the importance of such weapon systems in the maintenance of world peace. Although the multi-sonic missiles and aircraft of today were researched and developed as weapons, the knowledge gained in their research and development made possible, for instance, a spectacular achievement like Pioneer V. That space probe proved once and for all that man could communicate by radio over a distance of almost twenty five million miles through space. There was considerable doubt before among many sober scientists and engineers that such a feat was possible. It was made possible by a Thor Intermediate Range Ballistic Missile.

To the best of my knowledge, nobody previous to the author of this book has attempted to show the vast correlations and implications between weapon systems and peaceful world progress—vital as these are to public understanding and good faith. Perhaps it's because of Lloyd Mallan's unique background that he can see and make such correlations in a way that both layman and specialist will find valuable and fascinating. Author of MEN, ROCKETS, AND SPACE RATS, and many books on astronomy, satellites and missiles, most current of which are MAN INTO SPACE, FB 436, and AMATEUR ASTRONOMY HANDBOOK, FB 454, Lloyd Mallan is uniquely suited to this task.

The fact is that the realm of space science is with us, here and now, and this book is its basic primer. Mr. Mallan even includes the first complete official glossary of space missile terms for our guidance. This, then, is the new frontier, and Lloyd Mallan is our Horace Greely.

Kay Till —— Editor

america's **MIGHTIEST** missile

Watchdog of world peace and heavy workhorse
of scientific space research, the powerful Titan
strategic ICBM has made wars old-fashioned.

"TIME-ZERO" is the moment of launch for a missile in development at Cape Cañaveral. Before that moment is reached, many weeks, often months, of painstaking checkouts and sometimes heartbreaking setbacks go into preparing the missile for its flight down the Atlantic Missile Range. Yet at the Air Force Missile Test Center, which controls the range, Time-Zero is not the end of a test program. It is only a beginning.

For after the countdown comes the

(*Continued on page* 14)

At left, the mighty 2-stage Titan takes off from Pad 20 at Cape Canaveral to rise toward very edge of earth's atmosphere and curve with deadly accuracy into target-area 6,300 miles downrange.

Below, Titan with test version of operational re-entry vehicle has been serviced prior to launch. Gantry servicing tower is being lowered as 300-degree below zero F. liquid oxygen forms frost-sheath.

Unless noted otherwise, all photos in this chapter are from the Air Force Missile Test Center, Cape Canaveral, Florida; the Air Force Ballistic Missile Division, Inglewood, Calif.; and Denver, Col., Division of Martin Co.

Directly above, Titan's countdown is T plus some odd seconds: umbilical cables have disconnected and 110 tons of missile, tall as a 10-story office building, stands firmly on twin exhaust-flames of its double-barreled rocket engine. Thousands of tons of water are sprayed to cool the launching area. Servicing tower lies flat in foreground, out of the way.

Evolution of lethal accuracy and reliability of Titan can be traced to the Vanguard (above) and Viking rockets (at r.). Both were products of The Martin Company, which gained invaluable knowhow from them.

The Viking research rocket, shown on this page, was America's first heavyweight space workhorse—as Titan, also a Martin product, is destined to become in the near future on a much grander scale. Viking established high altitude and speed records for single-stage rockets. It uncovered unsuspected scientific information about the earth's upper atmosphere and was also the first big vehicle to take clear photos of earth from space. Another Viking "first": it was America's pioneer research rocket of native design for heavy payloads. Early to late modifications of Viking are pictured here. Vanguard came out of Viking as one of the world's most accurate and sophisticated rockets—a fact little recognized by the public because of a few unfortunate incidents.

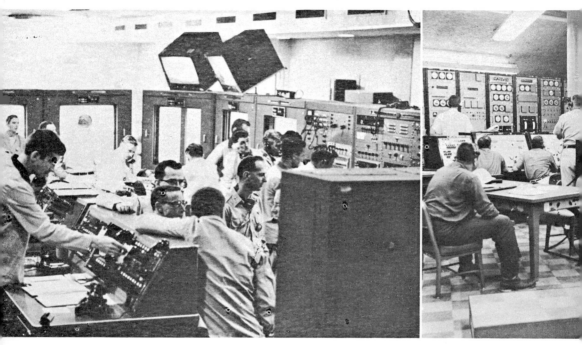

Test-flight of Titan starts at Lowry AFB, Colorado, which is near Martin Co.'s production facilities for the huge missile. Its 2 stages are loaded aboard a giant C-133 transport and airlifted to Cape Canaveral.

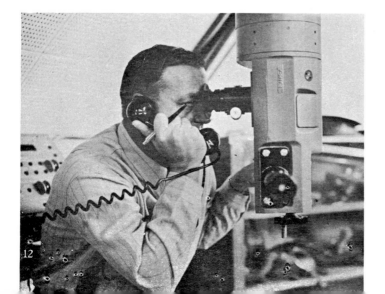

Photos above depict prelaunch activity in blockhouse control room, where electronic computers carry forth an automatic countdown. Television cameras surround the mighty missile as it sits on pad outside, so that technicians, engineers can keep close watch on it from the interior of their explosion-proof shelter of thick steel-reinforced concrete. Periscopes are also used for clear close-up details of the ICBM. At l., is controller at one of four periscopes. These scopes can be "zoomed" for both extreme close-in telephoto examination and drawn back for wide-angle inspection of the large sections.

12

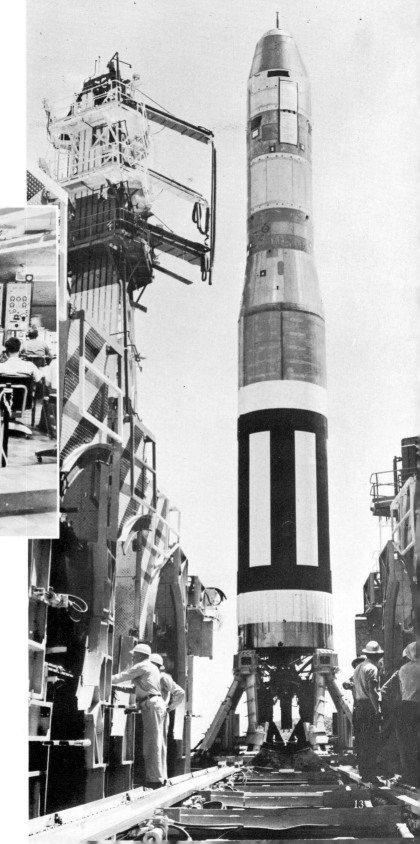

Below, across both pages, is fuller view of Titan control room. Note six TV screens in background beneath three clocks. One of these is set for GMT, or Universal Time. Series of numerical counters flash minutes, seconds left to T-O.

At r. is early Titan model waiting to be launched. Note instrumentation-boom atop the nose-cone used to gather data for relay to ground tracking stations. Each flight of the mighty missile gives scientists information by radio on temperatures, stability, the flow of fuel, pressures, G-forces, efficiency of separation of 2nd stage and dozens of other technical aspects that must be evaluated if gigantic missile is to be developed perfectly.

13

"count-up," during which "T" (for Time) is a succession of pluses instead of minuses. At approximately T-Plus-25-Minutes, in the case of an intercontinental ballistic missile, the engineers, scientists and technicians involved for weeks in preparing the missile will know whether or not it has met its test objectives. Several more hours or days may be required for detailed analysis of information radioed from the "bird" to ground tracking stations along the 5,500- to 6,300-mile range. But a mere 25 minutes gives the basic story in the case of an ICBM like Titan.

And this, too, is only a beginning.

Perfecting a missile cannot be accomplished in one apparently successful flight. There is always another set of test objectives, requiring another flight. The almost unbelievable complexity of the long-range birds, particularly, and the sheer perserverance and dedication of the men who conceive them, design them, build them and test them are a combination never before known, I am sure, in the world's extensive history of science. The fact that the long-range birds rise from their pads and soar at all is a tribute to the near-miracle of modern American technology. In fact, a week before starting to write this chapter, I was talking with Lt. General Bernard Schriever, the man whose own stubborn vision and faith made intercontinental-range ballistic missiles a reality. He told me that: "In 1954, many of our most respected scientists felt that it would be a waste of

Close-up of console for automatic countdown here shows clocks, counters, and warning lights. Amber light indicates function being checked, green light means function checks out, red denotes some malfunction.

Views on this page illustrate 2 moments of perfect Titan launch. This model of the ICBM carries the operational prototype re-entry vehicle, as shown.

At right: Author's photo

Below is Titan shortly after Time-Zero. At r., it begins its programmed roll, autopilots turning it over to set course for 2nd stage after 1st stage cutoff. Operational Titan II will use self-navigation.

These are the critical moments in test-flying any missile. The Range Safety Officer (above) at Cape Cañaveral sits tensely at his control console, watching Titan's course on the dynamic chart.

On the RSO's console are warning lights as well as switches. His fingers press lightly against 2 important switches, as seen at l. If "destruct" light glows red, fuel is cut off, missile destroyed.

money to try and perfect an ICBM. They said the big missiles could never fly with enough accuracy to strike a target five thousand miles away."

Backed up by a small group of scientists headed by Dr. John von Neumann, General Schriever took upon his shoulders one of the gravest responsibilities in contemporary military science. At the time, the General was Commander of the Air Force Western Development Division—now known as the Air Force Ballistic Mis-

But Titan, mightiest of America's missiles, stays right on course. Unusual photo above shows 1st stage cut-off and separation of 2nd stage. Titan hurtles toward fringe of space to span continents.

The big telemetry antenna at Cape Cañaveral turns slowly to lock-on Titan's radio signals. It follows the missile down the Atlantic Missile Range toward Grand Bahama, where another antenna picks up.

sile Division, at Inglewood, California. Today, because of his outstanding success, he is Commander of the entire Air Research and Development Command of the U. S. Air Force.

He and Dr. Von Neumann plus the scientist-members of the Strategic Missiles Evaluation Committee made up a group of less than a dozen men. The group, through almost inhuman dedication and persistence, finally convinced the Government of the United States that not only were ICBMs possible of development—but that without these missiles there would be little possibility of an assured world peace.

First of the ICBMs was Atlas. It was developed to operational status in five years.

Atlas is a one-and-a-half-stage missile. All three of its big rocket engines are ignited on the ground. Two of these are boosters attached to a "collar" that drops off when the missile reaches a certain altitude. It continues, propelled by its sus-

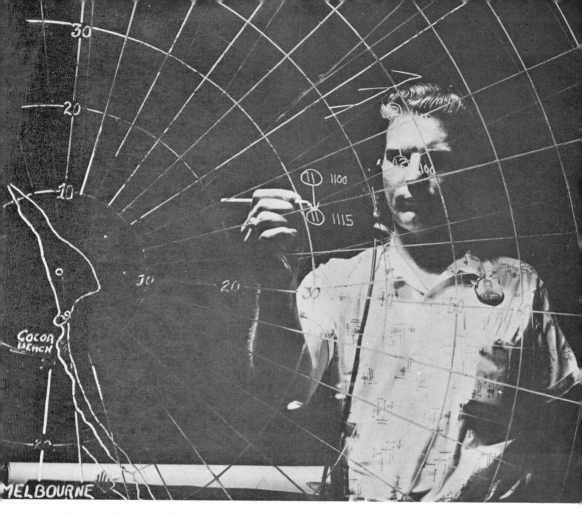

tainer engine into the ionosphere, where burnout occurs and its thermonuclear warhead detaches to fall in a long ballistic curve onto a target 5,000 to 6,000 miles away.

Titan was planned as a mightier missile. It can carry heavier warheads with greater reliability. It is a full two-stage missile, with an airframe made of an aluminum-copper alloy which has the thickness of a half-dollar. It is the first ICBM that can be launched from an underground silo, so that it is attack-proof from possible enemy ICBMs. Titan launch-crews can live in the underground silo-complex for long periods, until fall-out nuclear radiation from an enemy is dissipated through the atmosphere. The Titan launch-complex is virtually an underground city, with its own power generators, communications systems, food storage, water supply, etc. From experience gained in development of the Titan weapon system, the Atlas has profited. It is being adapted, as of this

writing, to below-the-surface silo launching as well.

Yet the Titan was being test flown only thirty-six months after ground was broken at the Martin-Denver plant to produce this ICBM on a practical, production-line basis.

In some part, this incredible record was due to things learned from the Atlas program. In large part, it was due to the experience with big rockets gained by The Martin Company, major associate contractor of the Titan program, and the cooperative experience inherent in the Air Force Ballistic Missile Division, which supervises all USAF ballistic missile programs, whether they be programs for short- or long-range missiles. The Martin Company produced America's first big research rocket, the Viking. This was a fully original departure from the design-techniques of the German V-2. With one third the rocket-thrust of the V-2, the Viking was at least twice as efficient as the German weapon. Out of Viking came the Vanguard

Radar at Grand Bahama Island picks up Titan and swings across sky to follow the giant weapon as it moves through space at more than 15,000 mph, toward a small target area over 5,000 miles downrange.

As Titan soars into the upper atmosphere big cameras still photograph it. These, along with radio give tracks to plotter, l., at Central Control.

Tracking of Titan continues as the mighty ICBM speeds upward, outward and over into a curve toward West Africa. Tracking ships and 11 land stations contact it before radar at Ascension Island (below) catches the mighty Titan and follows it to its ultra-accurate sea-impact.

19

rocket. Vanguard received a bad press because of a few unfortunate incidents, in which it appeared to "goof." Actually, Vanguard was in no condition to be launched—it had not been sufficiently checked out—when the U. S. Department of Defense ordered it off the pad prematurely because of the hysterical situation created by the successful Soviet launching of the first two sputniks. When Vanguard's schedule was permitted to go its normal way, the rocket placed three satellites into such perfect orbits that the average error was mere fractions of a per cent off the originally planned orbit. The three Vanguard-launched satellites are still orbiting today. One of them is calculated to last 2,000 years, another at least a century, and still another about 40 years. Not one of the five verified Russian sputniks can claim this. All of them have fallen out of orbit

As the flight-testing of Titan continues, to increase reliability of an already incredibly reliable weapon-system, production flows steadily along multiple assembly lines in The Martin Company's Titan factory at Denver. The plant is unique of its kind: Here, not only is the entire missile put together, but its stages are tested both individually and together. From assembly line production, the two stages move to a Vertical Test Facility where they are mated for the first time. At r., photo shows Titan in facility, "wrapped in "cellophane" for protection. Above, two production lines at l. show 1st stages, some with markings for ease of optical tracking. At far r. are 2nd stage lines.

(Continued on page 24)

Except for inset, these are USAF photos from American Machine & Foundry Co.

But flight-testing at the Cape is only to perfect missile as such. The huge "bird" is one equal part of a total system. It must next be "wedded" to its underground launching facility. For space research the mighty missile alone is sufficient and it bids high to become America's heavy-weight space workhorse for scientific research. As a weapon, however, it must be protected against enemy attack by storage in an underground "city," from where it can be launched. So testing continues at the Pacific Missile Range, which extends from Vandenberg AFB, California. Here Titan and its underground complex are tested together to perfect the total weapon system. The first version of Titan is lifted by elevator to the surface for firing, after having been fueled at the bottom of a silo 158 feet deep. Steel and concrete doors weigh 200 tons and are closed while Titan is stored. Photos show sequence of doors opening as huge missile is raised to the launch position above ground. Compare operational markings of Titan with those used in research-development testing, as shown in inset. Underground launchers are being built in many Western states by American Machine and Foundry Co. Titan II, a more advanced and powerful ICBM now in development, will be launched directly from inside silo. It will have storable fuels, permitting its launch with incredible speed after any warning.

and burned up in the earth's atmosphere within a matter of months. Sputnik III lasted longest—eighteen months.

So the forebears of Titan are formidable achievements in rocketry. While Titan itself bids high to become not only the greatest threat to the Kremlin's ambitions of world domination, but also to become the heavyweight workhorse of peaceful scientific space research of this decade. This latter aspect of Titan should undoubtedly change the whole future of mankind—for the better.

Quoting one man who should know what he is talking about, since he lives almost daily with Titan:

"Here's a missile, the Titan. Thousands of people have sweated like hell on it—to perfect it, make it work, so that it can be successfully launched and accurately hit a target across continents. And yet, if we ever have to use it—it failed. Your SAC missile crews, the engineers and scientists who test it, the contractor who makes it, are all dedicated to the production of a product—that they don't want to use. The mission of Titan is peace."

That was Major Tom Ellington, Chief of Information at the AFBMD.

On top of that, the power of the Titan missile is making wars old-fashioned. All future conflicts *should* be verbal. •

Aerial view of Titan I operational launch complex nearing completion at Lowry AFB, Colorado, is one of a number being built. At r. is photo-sequence of first Titan launch from underground, inside a silo. Modified Titan I was used to test system for advanced Titan II and was great success at Vandenberg AFB.

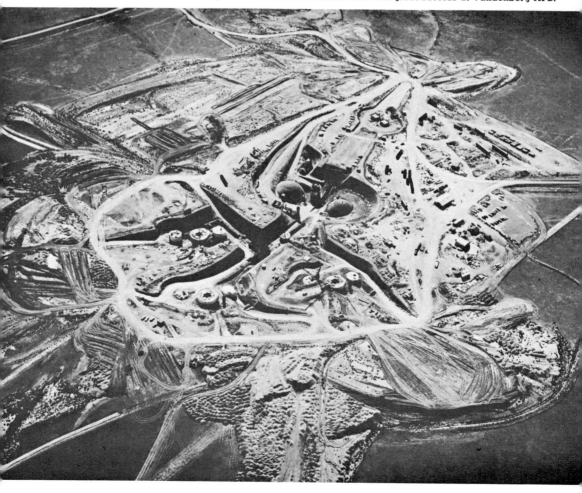

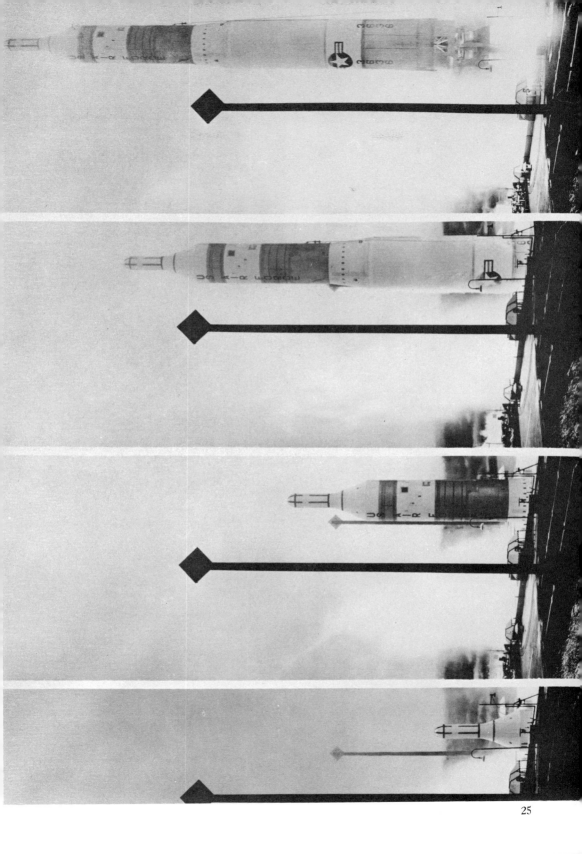

project **DYNA-SOAR**

and beyond

America's mightiest missile will boost this project
into a future where space science can send men to the planets.

"WE can visualize only tentatively and vaguely what man in space can do. But this we know—if space flight is ever to be practical, the pilot must be able to choose his times and points of take-off and landing."

That statement was made by Lt. General Roscoe C. Wilson, Deputy Chief of Staff for Development, U. S. Air Force. He was explaining the need for a new project called DYNA-SOAR at the Annual Night Fighters Luncheon, September 24, 1960. A few other statements the General made about the project that afternoon are little short of amazing, if we consider the vast range of technical problems that must be solved to make Project DYNA-SOAR a success. General Wilson had no doubt that it would be a success. The DYNA-SOAR problems, he said flatly, "run the gamut of the aeronautic and astronautic arts. Nevertheless, we expect to be flying DYNA-SOAR within the next three years.

"It is the first serious effort," he later said in private, "toward a vehicle which could, for example, be used to perform maintenance and repair of satellites; it could provide an extremely versatile observation or reconnaissance platform; it could inspect unknown objects; it also could provide a means of transporting personnel to and from space stations or laboratories; and it might perform the rescue of personnel in space."

Other experts working on the project feel that the future of DYNA-SOAR is limitless. It will be, among other things, the first Free World project to train a man to pilot a space ship in actual

At l., an actual photo of Titan symbolizes its space scientific mission as it appears to soar past the moon. Photo was made by an ROTI tracking camera just as moon was in right spot. At r., Martin Co. engineer, A. J. Kullas discusses plans for rocket booster portion of the Air Force DYNA-SOAR Project. Mr. Kullas directs engineering effort to modify Titan missile. Other project contractors are the Boeing Airplane Co. and the Aerojet-General Corp. NASA, civilian space agency, is cooperating fully by giving thousands of hours of free wind-tunnel time and instrumentation advice and control advice.

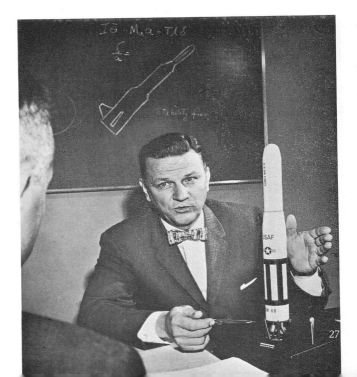

spaceflight conditions. Yet despite its future promise to peaceful scientific research, DYNA-SOAR could only have been a vague dream for another decade—without America's mightiest missile, the Titan.

A space ship has to be rocket-boosted into its environment. No other missile before Titan II was powerful enough to do this. In fact, the Air Force at first assigned Titan I to the project as booster. But there were limitations. Titan I was reserved only for Step I of the DYNA-SOAR program. This step is confined to sub-orbital flights down the Atlantic Missile Range off Cape Cañaveral, with landings on various island airstrips. After sufficient information is gained from these flights, Step II will follow with a series of short manned flights in orbit. Step III will be the actual conditioning of pilots to operate with full control in both an orbital and outer space environment. The second two steps demand considerably more rocket power than is available with Titan I, although Titan I at the time of this writing is America's most powerful, reliable and accurate long-range missile. Titan II, an advance-design ICBM, will be much more powerful and reliable than Titan I because of things learned during the research and development phases of its predecessor.

Here are artist's concepts of lift-off and 2nd stage ejection of DYNA-SOAR. Artist painted these before Air Force, which supervises total program, announced in January, 1961, that the booster would be Titan II, more powerful even than Titan I, the originally designated booster. Configuration of Titan II is slightly different: 2nd stage is exactly same width as 1st stage: no bullet-like taper is visible. DYNA-SOAR glider will be thrust into orbit at speed of 18,000 mph when the time comes, after many preliminary test flights at lower sub-orbital velocities.

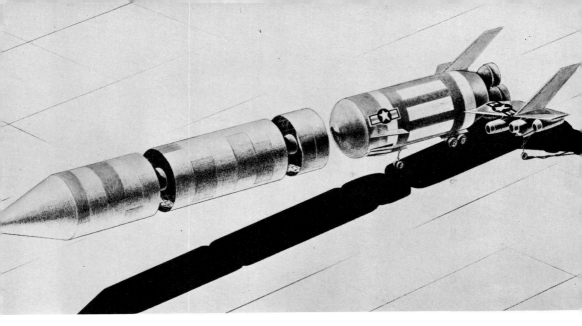

Above is Martin Co. design for an even more powerful Titan with 3 stages and recoverable 1st stage that can be flown back to earth and thus be reused at low cost for other missions.

Drawing at far r., conceived by Dr. John Housego at Martin-Denver, is kind of DYNA-SOAR of future. It uses a Nova-type 1st stage (4½ million thrust-pound engines), capable of landing manned capsule on moon with reserve power for return trip. At near r., is booster system to place payloads of from 12 to 15 tons in orbit. Atop final stage is package of modules, each of which is a part of space station. Below is a model of simulator to check out space pilots for space travel training.

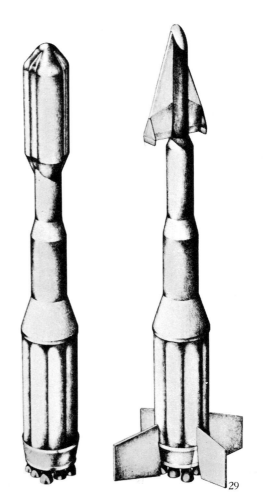

29

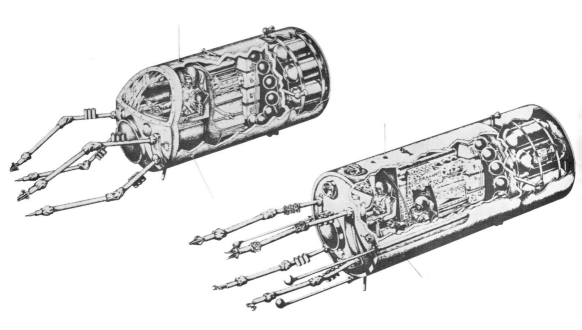

Above are two versions of a space-tug designed by Martin engineers at Denver. The tugs are an extension of Titan missile program, planning for the future. Tugs have servo "arms" and "hands" to manipulate construction materials to build space station. Each hand is really a tool (drill, clamp, hammer, welding torch) and can be interchanged with other tools. Tug at top is for 1 man, bottom tug carries 2 crewmen. Directly below is 1st stage toward completed space station: 3 tubular sections have been sent into orbit and put together by tugs. During launch into orbit, sections are folded on top of booster, as on page 29. Big "dish" is solar power-collector. Approaching is the 5-man ferry as developed out of DYNA-SOAR.

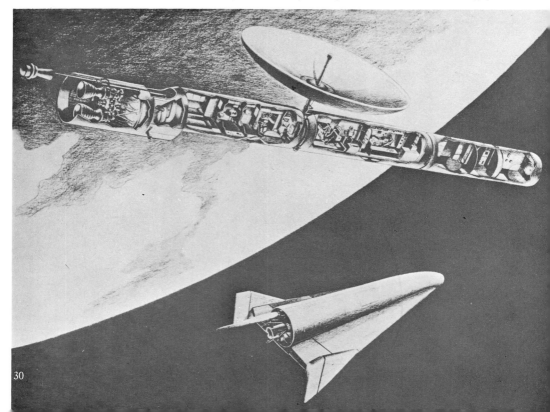

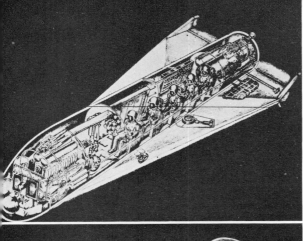

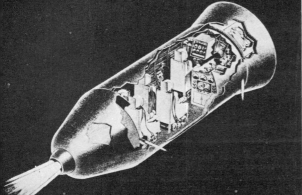

At top, l., is cutaway drawing of ferry vehicle shown at bottom of the facing page. Fondly called a "space jeep" by Martin engineers, it will be used to exchange crews on space station and carry supplies. Below are two other proposed kinds of space-jeep. One re-enters atmosphere ballistically, like a bullet, with retro-rockets to slow it down and parachutes to ease it in for final landing. The other is an extension of Mercury capsule, with room for 5 instead of 1 astronaut. Control would be limited on both these kinds of space-jeep. They might land almost anywhere, even have to be fished out of ocean. DYNA-SOAR-type jeep can be landed like an airplane, on a runway, and is preferred by Martin engineers.

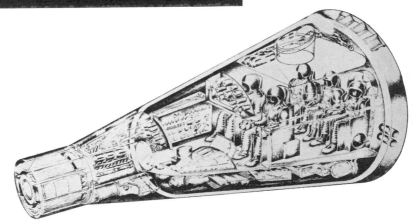

It is significant that in January, 1961, the Ballistic Missile Division of the Air Force ordered that Titan II be used to boost DYNA-SOAR in the Step I phase. This would indicate two important facts: 1. That the Titan II development program is well in hand. And 2. That the devastating Intercontinental Ballistic Missile designated SM-68B, popularly known as Titan II, may speed up the whole DYNA-SOAR program if it is selected as a booster for Step II.

The Martin Company's Denver Division builds and tests both versions of the Titan. Their Baltimore Division modifies the missile so that it can be used as a DYNA-SOAR rocket booster. Another significant event suggests that the mighty Titan could well become a transition-type booster for Step III. During 1960, the National Aeronautics and Space Administration awarded Martin three contracts relating directly to the Saturn Project. Saturn is a million-and-a-half-pound-thrust rocket booster with eight clustered engines. It is well

A 2nd stage of constructing the space station is shown here: cylindrical units have been sent into orbit and attached. Rotating arms now turn main living quarters to produce artificial gravity.

Close-up detail drawing here pictures how space-tugs put station together. Each big cylinder is a self-contained unit that can be sealed off from others for repair if it springs leak, decompresses.

under way in development at NASA's George C. Marshall Field Test Center at Huntsville, Alabama. The contracts awarded Martin make that company responsible for studying the *operational modes* of an *advanced* Saturn to determine how best to operate this huge rocket, designed for deep space exploration. Martin is also producing a small amount of Saturn booster hardware. The tie-in seems obvious. By placing the two-stage Titan SM-68B atop a Saturn and an advanced development of the DYNA-SOAR spacecraft atop the Titan, the United States would have a combination that could by 1966-67 send heavy manned payloads to the moon.

What, exactly, is DYNA-SOAR? It is the first actually working program that gives meaning to a new, widely used word: "aerospace." It is the wedding of a manned heavier-than-air machine with an unmanned automatic missile. The project name, DYNA-SOAR, is derived from a contraction of the phrase "dynamic soaring." In this case, dynamic soaring refers to the almost incredible maneuvers that will be required of a space pilot as he guides his craft back into the earth's atmosphere for a landing at a point of his choice. The space craft that rests in the nose of Titan II is also a delta winged glider designed to soar at hypersonic speeds without power. It is being designed and built by the Boeing Airplane Company. The Titan missile may boost the glider-space ship into orbit at 18,000 miles an hour, but when the pilot decides to leave his orbit and return to his home base, he's on his own. If he doesn't want to go up in smoke, quite actually, he has

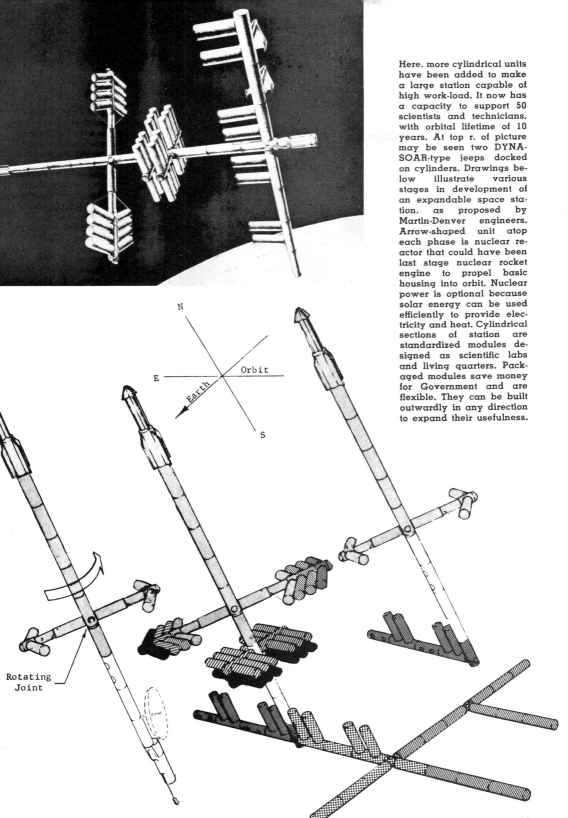

Here, more cylindrical units have been added to make a large station capable of high work-load. It now has a capacity to support 50 scientists and technicians, with orbital lifetime of 10 years. At top r. of picture may be seen two DYNA-SOAR-type jeeps docked on cylinders. Drawings below illustrate various stages in development of an expandable space station, as proposed by Martin-Denver engineers. Arrow-shaped unit atop each phase is nuclear reactor that could have been last stage nuclear rocket engine to propel basic housing into orbit. Nuclear power is optional because solar energy can be used efficiently to provide electricity and heat. Cylindrical sections of station are standardized modules designed as scientific labs and living quarters. Packaged modules save money for Government and are flexible. They can be built outwardly in any direction to expand their usefulness.

N

E   Orbit

Earth

S

Rotating
Joint

33

The Titan missile plus Project DYNA-SOAR have stimulated an intensive range of space research in The Martin Co. At their Denver Division, work goes on daily to determine how human beings can live and fly through space. Although this research is supported by company funds (an indication of a strong faith in the future), it is also a necessary competitive demand, since when DYNA-SOAR breaks through the final barrier to manned spaceflight, the industrial company with the most knowhow will get the most contracts. The Air Force knows no favorites, is only

At Martin-Baltimore, extensive experimentation goes on in fields of infrared research. Important as a possible guidance technique for future space ships, infrared radiations also guide missiles to targets.

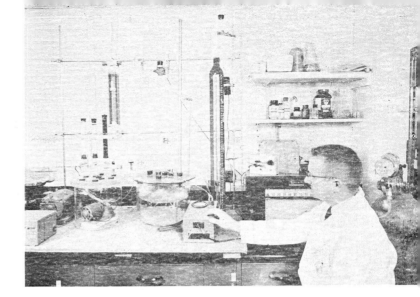

interested in results. Because of this, Martin got the DYNA-SOAR booster contract in a competition that included 7 major corporations. So a continuing research into all sciences vital to the future is necessary. At l., Ed Romano, agronomist at Martin-Denver, is seen in the space medicine greenhouse, where research in hydroponics and recycling gas-systems paves the way toward feeding men on the moon. Tomato plants grew from seed to 50 inches in 35 days. At r., Physiologist LeVora studies reduced pressures on small mammals used for test purposes.

to raise the nose of his ship just high enough to brake his tremendous speed, but not so high that the drag of his ship overcomes the lifting capability of its wings. If he holds the nose down too low, then his speed will increase to the point where friction, even in the thin upper atmosphere, will heat his ship to where it is blue-white like a meteor and vaporizes. These limits of aerodynamic lift versus drag and friction are known as the "corridor" through which the space pilot can safely return to earth.

Colonel Walter Moore, Program Director of Project DYNA-SOAR for the Air Force, describes the situation of a space pilot re-entering the atmosphere as follows:

"Let me compare this with the family automobile," he says, "if you have ever had the nerve to get it up to a hundred miles an hour. At a hundred miles an hour, the effect of an impact would be the same as if it had been dropped off the thirtieth floor of the Empire State Building. The DYNA-SOAR glider will be traveling at a speed equivalent to being dropped off a tower two thousand miles high. If it hit a brick wall, the glider and part of the brick wall would simply vaporize at temperatures several times those achieved on the surface of the sun (roughly 20,000 to 25,000 degrees Fahrenheit) . . .

"At first, the glider flies in the upper fringes of the atmosphere, using aerodynamic lift, like an airplane, while the drag or friction of the air slows it down. Even under this relatively gentle treatment, the nose and leading edges and skin of the glider reach red- and white-hot temperatures—just as the brake in your automo-

bile gets quite hot when slowing down suddenly from one hundred miles per hour. However, the glider must remain in this red-hot flight condition for tens of minutes to get rid of its tremendous energy—instead of the seconds involved in slowing down your automobile. A problem we call 'energy management' must be solved to arrive at the airfield which the pilot selects for his destination. The problem is like being given an automobile with a tank full of gas and told that you have to reach New York City. The throttle is locked in a wide-open position. You can use only the brakes to control the car. Along the highway are robbers waiting to kill you. The gas tank is fixed so that it will explode immediately on arrival in New York—if you have one drop of fuel left in it—and also kill you. If you use your brakes too much, you'll run out of gas on the highway and be at the mercy of those robbers. Now, all you can do is use the brake and choose your routes judiciously so that you arrive in New York with a wide-open throttle—but with a precisely empty gas tank.

"There are other equally tough situations to deal with. The glider must be made of materials able to withstand operating at temperatures like those inside a blast furnace . . ."

Among the many tough situations for the DYNA-SOAR pilot will be the violent vibration and noise he must endure during the Titan boost-phase of his journey. On his return trip, his communications equipment will be blacked out through a most critical part of his descent pattern: in the stratosphere (and maybe even higher) the speed of his glider will generate so much heat that electrons will be stripped from the air molecules, to form an electric "blanket" around him. He will not be able to receive advice from guidance or tracking equipment on the ground. These are only a small sample of the many complexities involved in perfecting the DYNA-SOAR spacecraft and mating the man to it safely. Yet regardless of such problems, Project DYNA-SOAR will succeed. As General Thomas D. White, Air Force Chief of Staff, said not long ago: "There are no barriers to further achievement other than those we impose upon ourselves. . . It is in the exploitation of advanced aerospace technology that we find our horizons unlimited."

One of the original objectives of DYNA-SOAR as stated by the U. S. Air Force was to create a vehicle piloted by a man with "sufficient maneuverability to make return from orbit a routine, nonadventurous, sup-

portable, *day to day* test or military operation." In other words, DYNA-SOAR's aim is to make routine from what is essentially spectacular.

The DYNA-SOAR Project differs extremely from NASA's Project Mercury, in which one of seven astronauts will be placed in a "ball" and shot around the earth for several hours. The astronaut will have only attitude-control over his capsule. He will not be able to land it at a chosen point. But what he learns about such controllability in a weightless condition will help the DYNA-SOAR pilot. The X-15 rocket-airplane is test-bed for D-S controls.

In keeping with United States policy of using outer space for only peaceful purposes, the Air Force states that DYNA-SOAR is merely an MTS (Military Test System) for pure research alone. But the first rocket-powered aircraft, the Bell

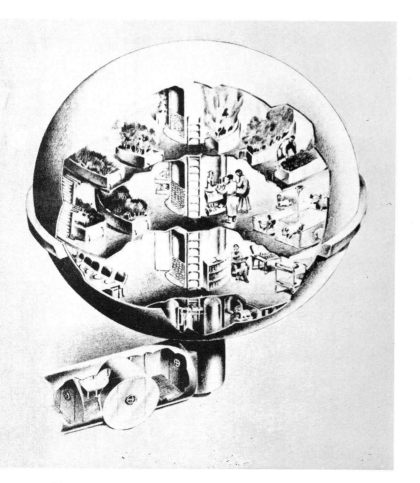

A lunar housing unit proposed by Martin-Denver scientists is shown here. Note the hydroponic gardens to grow food supplies quickly that will still be highly nutritive. Note also pens for fowl and cattle. A self-recycling atmosphere is also provided by focusing ultraviolet light on chlorella, a green scumlike algae that normally is found on the surfaces of stagnant ponds. When ultraviolet energy is focused on this algae it can transform toxic gases exhaled by humans and human waste products into oxygen for breathing and food high in basic protein values.

XS-1, was also an MTS when "Chuck" Yeager piloted it through the sonic barrier in October 1947. A few years later, military jet fighters were flying supersonically as routine. DYNA-SOAR's pilot, traveling in orbit at 18,000 miles an hour, could keep a close watch on potential enemies of the United States. He could rendezvous in space with other pilots for military purposes and he could carry heavy payloads of sky-to-ground anti-missile missiles or electronic countermeasure equipment to confuse enemy ICBM's. He could also carry scientific payloads to the moon or "truck" structural materials for an orbital labora-tory into space, where they could be put together by crews he would also transport.

In fact, "Buzz" Hello, veteran aeronautical engineer at The Martin Company calls DYNA-SOAR "a kind of space truck."

Returning to Colonel Moore: "Even before DYNA-SOAR flies," he says, "new designs for tomorrow's transportation will be on the drawing boards."

They already are there. Witness the advanced designs shown on these pages that have been developed by The Martin Company's Denver Division as part of the future programs for Titan and its ultimate descendents. •

At l. and below are models of a lunar housing simulator proposed by Martin's scientists. In miniature it would reproduce all the conditions to be found in the real thing on the moon. Scientists, in both practical and abstract ways, prove their concepts by evolving ingenious models shown.

The lunar housing proposal would permit scientists and technicians to live and work in the atmosphere-less environment of the moon, where intense radiations from the sun are a violent threat to man's existence and a slight puncture of his hermetically sealed synthetic earth-environment by a pea-sized meteorite would cause him actually to explode because of pressure-loss. Martin scientists have provided against this eventuality with an outer transparent shielding dome that can be repaired by men in pressurized suits if it should be damaged.

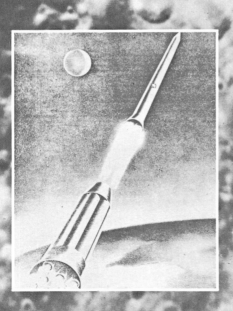

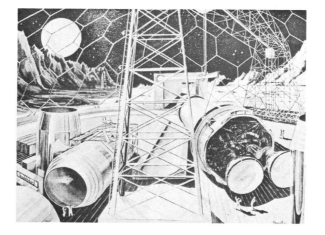

Against a background photo of the lunar surface made through a giant telescope of Mt. Wilson-Palomar Observatories are spread a display of far-out engineering studies already accomplished by engineers and scientists at Martin's Denver Division. These drawings as all others in this chapter, are not merely artist-concepts: they are actual projections of engineering plans. On the facing page, at top l., is "Boosted Arcturus," a space ship on the DYNA-SOAR plan that could carry payloads of 360,000 pounds to a minimum earth-orbit or 60,000 pounds to a soft landing on the moon. Its 1st stage booster would be a huge air-breathing engine, a turbo-ramjet combination. At l. center is Arcturus itself, boosted by two North American single-barreled rocket engines, each developing 1½ million pounds of thrust. It would consist also of 7 Titan 1st stage tank assemblies and be fueled by conventional liquid oxygen and kerosene or storable hypergolic fuels. It could carry several men one way to the moon, or one man on a round trip without refueling. At l. bottom is Saturn-Titan, where the 1st stage engine is a cluster of 8 rockets producing 1½ million pounds of thrust and the 2nd stage is a Titan II. At top of this page is a lunar space-terminal. At center l., is a lunar base patterned after the Martin lunar housing project, but exceedingly more elaborate. It'd be a city in itself. See cutaway drawing, center r.

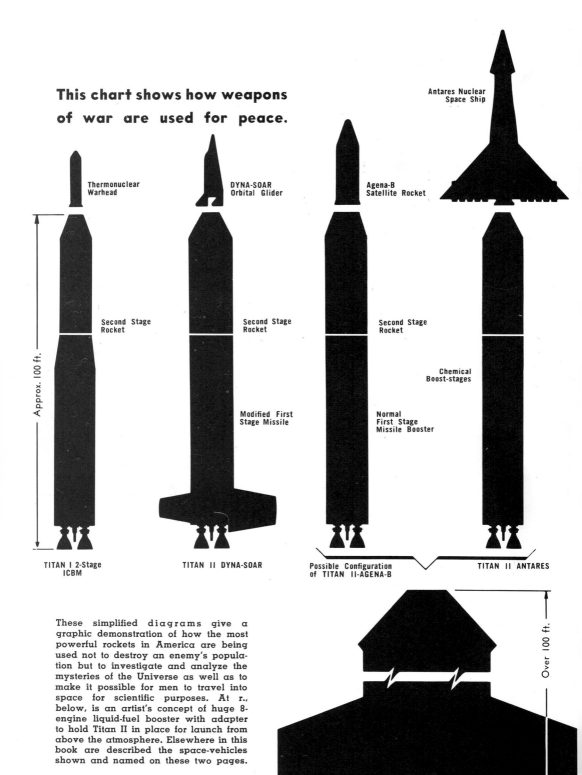

This chart shows how weapons of war are used for peace.

Thermonuclear
Warhead

Second Stage
Rocket

Approx. 100 ft.

TITAN I 2-Stage
ICBM

DYNA-SOAR
Orbital Glider

Second Stage
Rocket

Modified First
Stage Missile

TITAN II DYNA-SOAR

Agena-B
Satellite Rocket

Second Stage
Rocket

Normal
First Stage
Missile Booster

Possible Configuration
of TITAN II-AGENA-B

Antares Nuclear
Space Ship

Chemical
Boost-stages

TITAN II ANTARES

Over 100 ft.

These simplified diagrams give a graphic demonstration of how the most powerful rockets in America are being used not to destroy an enemy's population but to investigate and analyze the mysteries of the Universe as well as to make it possible for men to travel into space for scientific purposes. At r., below, is an artist's concept of huge 8-engine liquid-fuel booster with adapter to hold Titan II in place for launch from above the atmosphere. Elsewhere in this book are described the space-vehicles shown and named on these two pages.

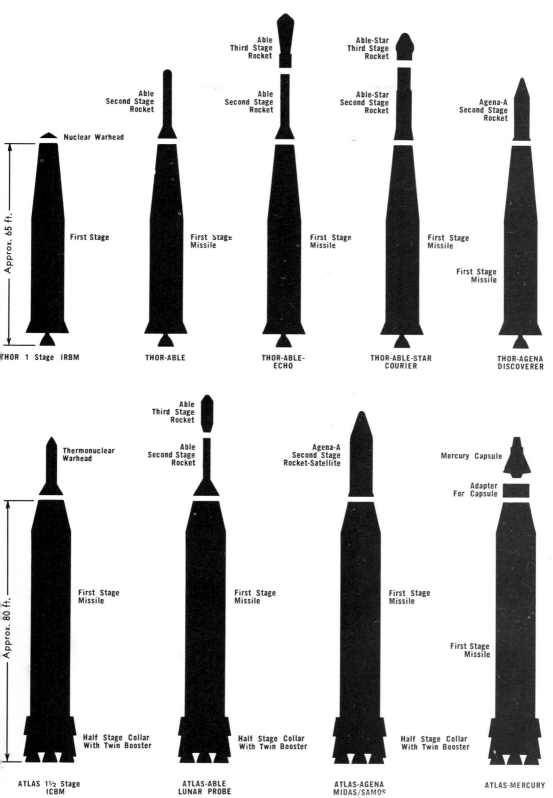

Approx. 65 ft.

Nuclear Warhead

First Stage

THOR 1 Stage IRBM

Able
Second Stage
Rocket

First Stage
Missile

THOR-ABLE

Able
Third Stage
Rocket

Able
Second Stage
Rocket

First Stage
Missile

THOR-ABLE-
ECHO

Able-Star
Third Stage
Rocket

Able-Star
Second Stage
Rocket

First Stage
Missile

THOR-ABLE-STAR
COURIER

Agena-A
Second Stage
Rocket

First Stage
Missile

THOR-AGENA
DISCOVERER

Approx. 80 ft.

Thermonuclear
Warhead

First Stage
Missile

Half Stage Collar
With Twin Booster

ATLAS 1½ Stage
ICBM

Able
Third Stage
Rocket

Able
Second Stage
Rocket

First Stage
Missile

Half Stage Collar
With Twin Booster

ATLAS-ABLE
LUNAR PROBE

Agena-A
Second Stage
Rocket-Satellite

First Stage
Missile

Half Stage Collar
With Twin Booster

ATLAS-AGENA
MIDAS/SAMOS

Mercury Capsule

Adapter
For Capsule

First Stage
Missile

First Stage
Missile

ATLAS-MERCURY

41

FLIGHT TIME OF THE GODS

The names given many space vehicles and
missiles are more prophetic than mythological.

Project Apollo is pictured above by an artist of
The Martin Co., one of three leading Space Age
manufacturers that have been awarded study contracts on project by NASA. Apollo was a god of
Ancient Greece, son of Clymene and Titan. This
is nicely appropriate, since Martin produces
the mighty Titan intercontinental ballistic missile.

Juno was the chief Roman goddess worshipped by
women. She was associated with Jupiter, who was
king, as queen of the heavens. The Juno missile
at left is ready to carry a payload toward the moon.

Photo by Charles Rogers, AF Missile Test Center

THE mythological gods of ancient Greece and Rome, in their universal wisdom, may have foreseen long before mortal man had the ability to do so, that their names would be blasted through unknown regions of blackest space to brighten human knowledge. This is always the goal of gods. It is now the goal of rockets that carry their names.

Thor, a god of Scandinavian myth, has more than expressed his personality in a rocket. He was said to be enormously strong, kind and generous to man but an enemy of all demons. Modifications of the Thor strategic missile have flung scientific laboratories millions of miles through space and around the earth from pole to pole. One of these, Pioneer V, proved that man could communicate two-way by radio over distances up to nearly 25 million miles.

The god Thor was identified with the Roman gods Jupiter and Zeus. The Jupiter C missile sent America's first successful satellite into orbit around the earth. The Nike-Zeus is being developed to protect the United States from long-range enemy missiles.

Atlas was a god of ancient Greece, whose mission was to hold the heavens and earth apart with his strength. The Atlas ICBM has catapulted into orbit satellites to watch an enemy and warn of his attack. One of these satellites was MIDAS, another god of ancient Greece, whose touch turned everything to gold.

Son of Clymene and Titan was Atlas. And now Titan has transcended his son in strength. The Titan ICBM stands today as the ultimate long-range ballistic missile in power and accuracy. It thus deters all enemies of freedom by the fury it could unleash. As heavyweight of future space research, it will benefit science and mankind. Already it has been chosen to hurl the first manned space ship into orbit and eventually this will lead to lunar round trip voyages.

Apollo was called the god of prophecy by Homer. According to the ancient Greeks, he vanquished the fleet Hermes in a foot race. Now Project Apollo is America's hope to send three men around the moon for important scientific studies. There are and will be other projects, all dependent for success upon rockets and space vehicles with names like Centaur, Nova and Saturn. Not all the names are those of ancient gods, but in one way or another they are connected with the gods, or the stars, or the enigmatic forces of nature that the ancients personified with their splendidly dramatic imaginations.

How did these colorful symbolical names come to be given today's missiles? They are really not official names, since most missiles are designated by a code number with letters indicating their mission. SM-68 is a Strategic Missile. TM-76 is a Tactical Missile. IM-99 is an Intercept Missile. GAR-8 is a Guided Air Rocket. So who is responsible for the more apt names of the missiles?

I asked this question of Lt. General Bernard Schriever, a man who should know, since he fathered practically all of America's most powerful missiles. He shrugged his shoulders and smiled. "I think," he said, "that individuals working for the various contractors are responsible. In the case of Titan, I'm almost certain that Joe Rowland of The Martin Company named it. But one way or another the names get around—and stick." •

The Apollo lunar spacecraft, planned to carry 3 crewmen on round trip between earth and the moon is shown here enroute among the stars. Protruding fan-shapes are solar-cell arrays to gather energy from sun for use aboard. Apollo was said to have been the first triumphant participant in Olympic games. Homer called him the "god of prophecy."

Art by Olivari—The Martin Co.

U. S. Army Ordnance Photo

Project Hermes missile at left is shown at blast off
from White Sands Proving Ground in early 1951.
It led to development of Redstone, which led to
Jupiter and Juno. Hermes was the Greek god of
communications, son of Zeus and Maia, who was
the daughter of Atlas, now a long-range missile.

Below is Jupiter, a strategic missile of USAF. An
earlier Jupiter C boosted America's first satellite,
Explorer I into orbit around the earth. Once
Jupiter was considered in ancient Rome as the
immortal protector, like the great Greek Zeus.

Photo by Parm, from Air Force Missile Test Center

Photo by McNearny—Air
Force Missile Test Center

It is fitting that this capsule
from the Mercury Project be
placed here exactly oppo-
site Hermes Project missile
on facing page. Mercury
was the god of ancient
Rome, the equivalent to
Hermes of ancient Greece.

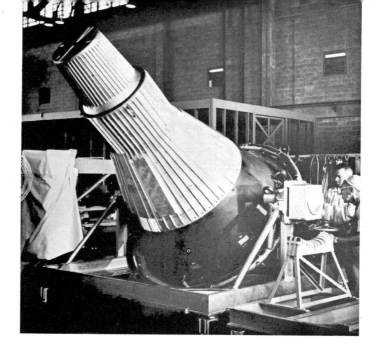

Engineering projections from Martin's Denver Division

Project Nova, originally a
USAF program, is now
NASA. It would be used to
fling great rocket payloads
far out through the reaches
of space. Its six turbojet engines plus its wings would
fly it back to earth. Signifi-
cantly, a "nova" is an expanding star, traveling at
many thousands of miles
per sec. outward in space.

Another in-house project of
The Martin Co. is a project
of the Denver Division's
Advanced Programs Sec-
tion. It is called "Aldeb-
aran" appropriately and
drawing here gives a faint
idea of size of its rocket
engine and space ship,
alongside an ocean liner.
Designed to land in ocean
after gliding back through
atmosphere, it is named for
a giant red star, 50 times
larger than our sun in diameter and one of 20
brightest stars in the sky.

official glossary of SPACE-MISSILE TERMS

A veritable encyclopedia of valuable information; the layman as well as engineers and missile "buffs" will find this fascinating.

IRBM—The Thor Intermediate Range Ballistic Missile operates with Strategic Air Command.

RCA Photo Lab, AF Missile Test Center

ABLATION—The melting of nose cone materials during re-entry into the earth's atmosphere at hypersonic speeds.

ABMA—Abbreviation for Army Ballistic Missile Agency. A research and development agency of U.S. Army Ordnance Missile Command, with its headquarters and primary facilities at Huntsville, Alabama. (A field office of ABMA is located at AFMTC.)

ABSOLUTE ZERO—Theoretical temperature at which all thermal motion or heat action stops (approximately —273.16°C or —459.69°F).

AERODYNAMICS—That field of dynamics dealing with the motion of bodies relative to the air and the forces that act upon them, especially as related to flight.

AERODYNAMIC MISSILE—A missile whose weight is sustained in flight through the use of wings or similar aerodynamic lifting surfaces. Also called a "cruise missile," it is an aircraft-type vehicle designed for military purposes. (The SNARK, BOMARC and MATADOR are aerodynamic, or cruise missiles.)

AEROPAUSE—A portion of the upper region of the atmosphere which does not provide aerodynamic support for either manned or unmanned flight.

AFBMD—Abbreviation for Air Force Ballistic Missile Division. A division of Headquarters, Air Research and Development Command, it is responsible for the development of operational ballistic missiles of both intermediate and intercontinental ranges. Its headquarters is located at Inglewood, California. (A field office, the Directorate of Air Force Ballistic Missile Tests is located at AFMTC.)

AFMTC—Abbreviation for the Air Force Missile Test Center. The ARDC center charged with maintaining and operating the Atlantic Missile Range to conduct Department of Defense missile tests, and to gather performance data on missiles tested. The AFMTC headquarters is at Patrick Air Force Base, Florida; its missile launching site is approximately 18 miles north of Patrick at Cape Canaveral.

AIRFOIL—Any aerodynamic surface designed to obtain a reaction from the air through which it moves. An aileron, wing, rudder or similar device is an airfoil.

AIRFRAME—The assembled structural and aerodynamic components of an aircraft or missile which support the different systems and subsystems integral to the missile or aircraft.

APOGEE—The high point in an orbit. The apogee refers to the maximum distance away from the earth of an orbital vehicle. It is the opposite of perigee, or point of nearest approach.

AFSC—Abbreviation for the Air Force System Command. A major air command of the USAF, it is charged with maintaining qualitative superiority of Air Force weapons and equipment through research and development in basic and applied science. Its headquarters is at Andrews Air Force Base, Maryland.

ASKANIA—A cine-theodolite, which is a high precision optical instrument used in the ballistic instrumentation of guided missile tests. ("Askania" is the name of the German company which manufactures theodolites.) The cine-theodolite is used in pairs or various combinations to survey the position of a missile in flight. The instrument consists of an accurate transit type surveying device which automatically records the azimuth and elevation angles together with a picture of the direction of pointing; thus, tracking errors can be corrected and a true direction to the target determined.

ASSEMBLY—A combination of parts or subassemblies that may be taken apart without destruction which has no applica-

FOREWORD

This Air Force Ballistic Missile Division Glossary of Missile and Space Terms is the initial installment of United States Air Force recommended terminology and definitions in the space-missile area. It has been prepared to meet expressed needs for standardized communication and to provide a common ground on which established Air Force positions in these area may be based.

In view of the importance of missile and space activities, the need for a uniform set of terms and definitions is self-evident. This need will continue to grow. It is hoped that the Glossary will keep pace and will provide the basis for mutual understanding and recognition of applicable terminology.

Terminology and definitions for this Glossary have been supplied by agencies in the Air Force Ballistic Missile Division Complex. Primary contributions are made by personnel of the Division, the Ballistic Mis-

sile Center of the Air Materiel Command, and the Office of the Assistant Commander-in-Chief, Strategic Air Command (SAC MIKE). Special recognition is due the Terminology Control Branch of the Directorate of Administrative Services, Headquarters USAF for their compilation of the original listing of space-missile terms and definitions. The Glossary itself is prepared and issued by the Office of the Director of Administrative Services, AFBMD.

By internal agreement this Glossary represents the official AFBMD position on space-missile terms. The terminology and usages defined herein are prescribed for AFBMD usage, both internally and wherever the Air Force is represented in negotiations with other agencies. Moreover, the Terminology Control Branch, Directorate of Administrative Services, Headquarters USAF has sanctioned this Glossary for Air Force-wide usage.

The Editors of this Glossary fully recognize the dynamic nature of missiles and space terminology. It is fluid and expanding; it is subject to constant change and refinement. Consequently it is difficult at this stage to provide terms and definitions which will meet every need. In view of this situation it is the desire of the agencies concerned to expand and amplify the Glossary. Users are encouraged to submit missile-space terminology and definitions, including recommended changes, corrections, or additions, to the Director of Administrative Services, Air Force Ballistic Missile Division, Air Force Unit Post Office, Los Angeles 45, California.

O. J. Ritland
Major General, U.S.A.F.
Commander

Editor's note: The original Ballistic Missile Division Glossary has here been considerably expanded by incorporating into it an equally important official glossary compiled more recently by Headquarters, Air Force Missile Test Center, Cape Cañaveral, Florida. This is, therefore, the most complete official glossary available on missile research and development terms. R.G.

tion or use of its own but is essential for the completeness of a more complex item with which it is combined.

ASTRONAUTICS—The art or science of designing, building, and operating space vehicles.

ATLANTIC MISSILE RANGE—The better than 5,000 miles of ocean area over which the Air Force Missile Test Center flight tests missiles and related equipment. The "Range," extending from Cape Cañaveral, Florida, to Ascension Island in the South Atlantic Ocean, is instrumented with a series of island bases tracking stations and ocean range vessels to gather performance data on missiles, rockets and satellites tested over its facilities. (See OCEAN RANGE VESSEL, below.)

ATLAS—An Air Force surface-to-surface ICBM manufactured by the Astronautics Division of Convair. Also called SM-65, it is currently operational and is also used to boost SAMOS/MIDAS into orbit.

ATMOSPHERIC BRAKING—The action of atmospheric drag in decelerating a body that is approaching a planet; can be deliberately used, where sufficient atmosphere exists, to lose much of the vehicle velocity before landing.

ATTITUDE—The position of an aircraft or missile as determined by the inclination of its axis to some frame of reference. If not otherwise specified, this frame of reference is fixed to the earth.

AZUSA—An electronic tracking system which collects continuous precision data on the position of a missile in flight. The system includes eight ground antennas, formed in a cross, and a transponder carried in the missile. The transponder receives signals from the ground station and, by "answering" them, reflects the initial raw data for use. In addition to its data collection function, the AZUSA serves (at AFMTC) as the data source for the impact predictor (see IMPACT PREDICTOR).

BACKUP ITEM—(For R&D programming purposes.) An additional item under development to perform the general functions of another item under development. The item may be secondary to an identified primary item or a parallel development to enhance the probability of success in performing the general function. The BACKUP ITEM may occur at any point in the development cycle from PART to SYSTEM and/or any type of END ITEM.

BALLISTIC MISSILE—A type of missile, either guided or unguided, which is powered only for the brief, early portion of its flight and then travels most of its trajectory in a free-fall ellipse. A thrown rock is a ballistic missile. If guided, a bal-

ARMAMENT ROCKETS—At r., F-100 Super Sabre fires 114 2.75-inch rockets at tactical ground target.

ANTI-MISSILE MISSILE—Nike-Zeus is Army missile designed to destroy ICBM re-entry warheads.

Army Chief of Ordnance Research

listic missile will ordinarily be controlled during the powered phase of flight only. There is no officially accepted definition for a ballistic missile, but it generally refers to any vehicle whose major portion of flight is in free fall in the manner of a projectile. (The ATLAS, TITAN, MINUTEMAN, THOR, JUPITER, PERSHING and POLARIS are ballistic missiles.)

BALLISTIC TRAJECTORY—The curved portion of a missile trajectory traced after the propulsive force is cut off and the body is acted upon only by gravity, aerodynamic drag and wind.

BASE COMPLEX—An air base for support of Air Force units consisting of landing strips and all components or related facilities for which the Air Force has operating responsibility, together with interior lines of communication and the minimum surrounding area for security.

BATTLESHIP TANK TESTS—Propulsion system tests using heavy walled propellant tanks to investigate problems in the marriage of the engines and the propellant feed system. The heavy walled "battleship" tanks are needed in order to permit repeated pressurization of the tanks to a level high enough to simulate the acceleration head achieved in actual flight.

BIRD—Missile jargon for a missile, rocket, or missile test vehicle.

BLANKETING—The process of having a desired signal blanketed, or eliminated from reception, by the presence of an overriding, stronger undesired signal.

AF Air Proving Ground Center

BLOCKHOUSE—A reinforced concrete structure, located near the missile launching pad, which houses special control systems used by operating personnel to effect the remote control launching of a missile.

BOILOFF—The vaporization of liquid oxygen as the temperature of the propellant mass rises during exposure to ambient conditions of the missile tank or other containers.

BOMARC—An Air Force surface-to-air long-range interceptor missile developed by Boeing. Also known as the IM-99, it is guided to its target by radio command and radar in conjunction with the SAGE (semiautomatic ground environment) system of the Air Defense Command.

BOOSTER ROCKET—1. An auxiliary rocket which provides additional thrust to assist the normal propulsive system of a missile or rocket in some phase of its trajectory or flight path. (Twin boosters are attached to the external surface of a SNARK to give added power on takeoff; shortly after the missile is airborne, they are dropped and it continues its flight on its own jet engine power.) 2. In another application, a booster may be considered the first-stage propulsion system which powers the launch and initial trajectory phase of a multistage vehicle.

BUILDUP—The process of attaining prescribed strengths of units and prescribed levels of vehicles, equipment, stores and supplies. Also may be applied to the means of accomplishing this process.

BURNOUT—1. The time at which a jet or rocket engine ceases to burn because of the exhaustion of fuel. The term is distinct from "cutoff," which implies an intentional command cessation of burning. 2. The rupturing of a combustion chamber through excessive heating.

BURNOUT VELOCITY—The velocity attained at the time the propellant(s) is (are) exhausted or cutoff occurs. See BURNOUT and CUTOFF.

CAPTIVE TEST—A test conducted while the missile is secured to a test stand. Primarily intended to verify proper operation of the propulsion and flight control subsystems under full thrust conditions. May also test the operation of any or all of the remaining airborne subsystems. Not necessarily a FLIGHT READINESS FIRING, which see. Also see STATIC TEST, listed on page 65, column 2.

CELESTIAL GUIDANCE—The guidance of a missile or vehicle by reference to celestial bodies. (The missile is equipped with gyroscopes, telescopes, mechanically or electrically recorded navigational tables, computers, and other instruments and devices that sight stars, calculate position, and direct the missile. The SNARK, for example, is equipped with CELESTIAL GUIDANCE.)

CHARACTERISTIC LENGTH—In propulsion, the ratio of the chamber volume to its nozzle throat area. A measure of the length of travel available for the combustion of the propellants.

CHECKOUT—A sequence of operational and calibrational tests needed to determine the condition and status of a weapon system. Automation is frequently used to shorten the checkout time cycle.

COMMAND DESTRUCT—A system which destroys the missile, actuated on command of the Range Safety Officer, whenever missile performance degrades enough to be a safety hazard.

COMMAND DESTRUCT SIGNAL—A radio signal initiated by the Range Safety Officer that detonates an explosive in a missile or rocket to destroy the vehicle in flight.

COMMON ITEMS—Those Air Force items of supply with application to two or more weapon systems, subsystems, support equipment, including components and spares related thereto.

COMPONENT—A combination of units or parts which together may be functionally independent of, or an independent entity within, a complete operating module or subsystem, but which provide a self-contained function necessary for proper module, subsystem or system operation.

CONDENSATION TRAIL—A visible cloud streak, usually brilliantly white in color which trails behind a missile or vehicle in flight under certain conditions. It is caused by the formation of water droplets or sometimes icy crystals due to the sudden compression, then expansive cooling, of the air through which the vehicle passes. Although spectacular, these trails may interfere with visual tracking of a missile. They are popularly called *contrails* from a contraction of the two words; also, they are sometimes called *vapor trails*.

CONSOLE—Term applied to a grouping of controls, indicators and similar electrical or mechanical equipment which is used to monitor readiness of and or control specific functions such as missile checkout, countdown, or launch operations. Consoles are usually designed around desklike arrays.

COTAR—Abbreviation for *CO*rrelation *T*racking *a*nd *R*anging. COTAR is an electronic tracking system using omnidirectional antennas and a transponder in the missile to measure positions of a missile in flight.

COUNTDOWN—The numbered and timed

AF Ballistic Missile Division

COUNTDOWN CONSOLE—A control panel electrically tied to missile shows status of preparation.

CONTINENT-TO-CONTINENT RANGE MISSILE—Titan is a super long-distance heavy-duty giant.

USAF photo from The Martin Company

sequence of events and checks that must be conducted during the last few hours before a test missile is launched. (Serving to check countless switches and valves, to warm up and start missile subsystems, to check the readiness of launch facilities and range stations, to load propellants aboard the missile, etc., the countdown normally lasts about six to eight hours.) It is measured in terms of T-TIME (T minus time prior to initiation of engine start sequence and T plus time thereafter). Is also used to describe the step-by-step process leading to captive tests, battleship tank tests, flight readiness firings and mock firings.

CREW—A group of specialists who perform simultaneous and sequential duties and tasks involved in the accomplishment of an assigned operation.

CUTOFF—The shutting off of a liquid or solid propellant combustion process of a rocket engine, thereby causing a rapid drop toward zero thrust. In large rocket engines a significant impulse may occur during the delay from full thrust to zero thrust.

DATA REDUCTION—The process wherein raw data gathered by various electronic and optical devices on a test missile's flight are fed through automatic reduction machines to provide usable information on the missile's performance. (This information is subsequently compiled in a Flight Test Report for evaluation purposes.)

DEPOT-LEVEL MAINTENANCE—(In a Missile Unit Sense.) Maintenance performed on Air Force material requiring major overhaul or a complete rebuild of parts, assemblies, subassemblies and end items, including the manufacture of parts, modifications, testing, reclamation as required. Depot-level maintenance serves to support organizational maintenance by providing technical assistance and performing that maintenance beyond the Strategic Missile Squadrons' responsibility and/or capability. Depot-level maintenance provides stocks of serviceable equipment by use of more extensive facilities for repair than available in organizational-level maintenance activities.

DESTRUCT—The deliberate action of detonating or otherwise destroying a rocket, missile or vehicle after it has been launched, but before it has completed its course. Said of friendly missiles esp. during test flights. (DESTRUCTS are executed when the missile gets off its plotted course or functions in a way as to become a hazard.) See COMMAND DESTRUCT.

DESTRUCT LINE—A graphic representation drawn on a geographical map to show the boundary which a missile must not cross during flight. These lines are all superimposed on maps, in pairs, and together define the space corridor in which missiles may fly. A missile which moves beyond the destruct line or either side is destroyed by the Range Safety Officer.

DESTRUCTOR—An explosive or other device for intentionally destroying a missile or rocket, or a component thereof.

DEVELOPMENT—The application of known scientific facts, techniques, materials, and physical laws to the creation of new or improved material or methods of military use.

DIGITAL COMPUTER—A complex electronic mechanism which performs mathematical computations.

DOPPLER EFFECT—The apparent change in frequency of a sound or radio wave, reaching an observer or a radio re-

TACTICAL-RANGE MISSILE—Pershing is versatile, can destroy land forces nearby or very far away.

Army photo from The Martin Company

ceiver, caused by a change in distance or range between the source and the observer or the receiver during the interval of reception.

DOVAP—An abbreviation for "*DOppler Velocity and Positions.*" DOVAP is a system consisting of a ground transmitter station and a series of ground receiving stations which operate in conjunction with a transponder in the missile. Function of the system is to obtain information on the position and velocity of the missile. The doppler effect principle (above) is employed. (See TRANSPONDER).

DRONE—A remotely controlled pilotless aircraft. (Drones are employed at AFMTC as aerial targets for interceptor missiles being tested.)

ELECTRONIC DATA PROCESSING CENTER (EDP CENTER)—A center that maintains automatically operated equipment, including computers, designed to simplify the use and interpretation of the mass of data gathered by modern instrumentation installations or information collection agencies.

END ITEM—A final combination of products, component parts and/or materials which is ready for its intended use, e.g., turbo pump, guidance system, crash truck, missile, aircraft engine.

ENGINEERING CHANGE PROPOSAL (ECP)—The medium utilized by the contractor for formally proposing and processing engineering changes affecting safety, deviation from contract specifications, requirements for performance interchangeability, appreciable weight or cost, or which requires action regarding retrofit, service bulletins, or technical orders.

ENGINEERING DRAWINGS—Drawings usable for the complete fabrication, inspection and identification of all details, assemblies and components of the finished product for which these drawings are made. These drawings do not include production drawings which are made in addition to engineering drawings on the missile or support system which are used solely for the contractor's plant facilities.

ENGINEERING SUPPORT PERSONNEL—Those individuals expending effort in support of the development program such as draftsmen, technicians, mechanics, technical secretaries, etc. This category of personnel can be utilized as "direct manpower" or "indirect manpower."

ENTIRE JOB BASIS CONCEPT—(In Contracting.) In a contract written on an "entire job" basis, the contractor agrees to *complete* within a reasonably accurate estimated period of time, research and development which will require, in addition

to engineering reports, the delivery of such hardware as flyable experimental model(s), breadboard model(s), unique spare parts, and special test equipment.

ESCAPE VELOCITY—The minimum velocity required for a rocket, missile, or other object to escape the gravitational attraction of a planet or other spatial body. The earth's escape velocity is nearly seven miles per second (about 25,000 mph); the moon's is about 1½ miles per second (5,-400 mph).

ESSENTIAL REPAIR—Only those repairs, bench checks, functional checks, adjustments, tests, and work necessary to ensure that an end item is restored to a serviceable condition and will efficiently accomplish its intended purpose. ESSENTIAL REPAIR prohibits expending manhours accomplishing unnecessary disassembly and complete overhaul.

EXOSPHERE—The outermost fringe of the earth's atmosphere.

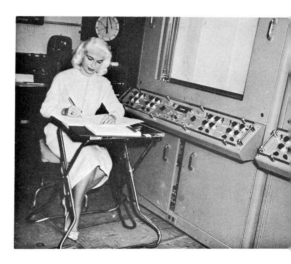

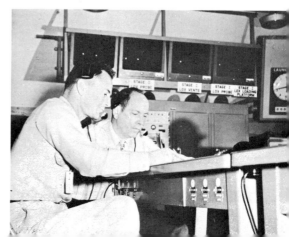

EXOTIC FUEL—New fuel combinations, currently under development, intended to provide greater thrust than propellants now in use.

EXPLORER—The first U.S. earth satellite to be successfully placed in orbit. Developed by the ABMA and the Jet Propulsion Laboratory of the California Institute of Technology, a modified JUPITER-C rocket consisting of four stages was used as the launching vehicle. Also called "1958 Alpha," it was launched from Cape Canaveral, Florida, at 10:48 p.m. (EST), January 31, 1958.

FBM—Abbreviation for Fleet Ballistic Missile (e.g., the POLARIS).

FLIGHT READINESS FIRINGS (FRF)—Missile system tests of short duration conducted with the propulsion system operating while the missile is secured to the launcher. Such tests are performed to determine (to the extent possible) the readiness of the missile system and launch facilities prior to flight test. See CAPTIVE TEST and FLIGHT TEST.

FLIGHT TEST—Test of an aircraft or missile by actual flight or launch. FLIGHT TESTS, usually heavily instrumented, are planned to achieve specific test objectives and gain operational information on the vehicle.

FIRST MOTION—In guided missile range terminology, the first indication of motion of the missile or test vehicle from its launcher. It is synonymous with "take-off" for vertically launched ballistic missiles. (See LIFTOFF.)

FLAC—An abbreviation for FLORIDA AUTOMATIC COMPUTER. It is a digital computer used at AFMTC for data reduction purposes. (The original Florida Automatic Computer was designed and constructed by a civil service worker formerly employed in data reduction at AFMTC.)

GANTRY—A crane-type structure, with platforms on different levels, used to erect,

DATA REDUCTION—Test information radioed by missile is analyzed and correlated from coded raw data by electronic computers. Girl at l. is mathematician.

AF Missile Test Center

GANTRY—Crane-like servicing tower, as shown at r. Purpose is to give crew members an ease of access to the various levels of a big missile so that parts can be worked on as well as checked. Gantry here is for Atlas. Other kinds follow.

AF Ballistic Missile Division

GOE/GSE—Ground Operational Equipment/Ground Support Equipment. An ICBM is only one important part of a total weapon system. At l., civilian engineer of Titan Program for Space Tech Labs (r.) and AF engineer check out GOE in control room of underground silo launch complex. Silo is 158' deep.

AF Ballistic Missile Division

assemble, and service large rockets or missiles. It may be placed directly over the launching site and rolled away before firing.

GIMBALLED MOTOR—A rocket motor mounted on a movable frame, or gimbal. It corrects for pitching and yawing rotation movements to steer a missile.

GRAIN—The body of a solid propellant, formed in a particular shape and size to provide even burning.

GROUND HANDLING EQUIPMENT— That equipment which is used to accomplish a prime mover function, e.g., a gantry, a missile transporter, forklift.

GROUND START—A propulsion starting sequence through ignition to main stage which is initiated and cycled through to completion on the ground. This is in contrast to an in-flight or "air" start where the starting sequence and power buildup occur in flight at sometime after launch. In large rocket vehicles this ground start is commonly effected from pressurized propellant tanks external to the missile, permitting the vehicle to take off with its internal propellant load intact.

GUIDANCE—The process of intelligent maneuvering which causes a missile or other vehicle to reach a specified destination. Guidance is accomplished by control in two phases: *attitude control* and *path control*. The general term *guidance* includes the entire scheme, i.e.,—sensing devices, computers, and the servo systems necessary to convert the calculated guidance commands into vehicle response. Guidance may be separated into phases of the flight path as: *initial, midcourse,* and *terminal.* Essentially there are eight basic guidance systems: *preset, terrestrial reference, radio navigation, automatic celestial navigation, inertial, command, beam rider,* and *homing.*

GUIDANCE, BEAM RIDER—A scheme of guidance in which the missile follows a radar beam to the target by means of on-missile computers and controls which are sensitive to radar beams.

GUIDANCE, CELESTIAL—A form of navigation using the celestial bodies as reference points much the way early sailors used stars as navigational aids.

GUIDANCE, COMMAND—A system of guidance in which the vehicle is directed in its flight path by radio commands from a ground station.

GUIDANCE, HOMING—A system wherein a missile steers itself toward a target by means of a self-contained mechanism which is activated by some distinguishing characteristic of the target.

AF Ballistic Missile Division

GANTRY/MINUTEMAN—Servicing towers vary greatly from missile to missile as do configurations.

GUIDANCE, INERTIAL—A system independent of information obtained from outside the missile, the sensitive elements of which system make use of the principle of Newton's second law of motion.

GUIDANCE, INFRARED—A method for reconnaissance of targets and navigation using infrared heat sources.

GUIDANCE, MIDCOURSE—The guidance applied to a missile between the termination of the launching phase and the start of the terminal phase of guidance.

GUIDANCE, PRESET—A technique of missile control wherein a predetermined path is set into the control mechanism of the vehicle and cannot be adjusted after launching.

GUIDANCE STATION EQUIPMENT— The ground-based portion of the ballistic missile guidance system necessary to provide ground-based guidance during missile flight; GUIDANCE STATION EQUIPMENT specifically includes the tracking radar, the rate measuring equipment, the data link equipment, and the computer and test and maintenance equipment integral to these items.

GUIDANCE SYSTEM—A system which measures and evaluates flight information, correlates this with target data and converts the resultant into parameters necessary to achieve the desired flight path of a missile and communicates this data in the

GANTRY/THOR—Dramatic view of this IRBM servicing platform suggests numerous parts to be checked.

form of commands to the missile flight control system. A GUIDANCE SYSTEM may be self-contained within the missile, or the guidance function may be performed by various combinations of ground and airborne components.

GUIDANCE, TERMINAL—The guidance applied to a missile between the termination of the midcourse guidance and impact.

GUIDANCE, TERRESTRIAL REFERENCE—A technique of missile control wherein the predetermined path set into the control system of a missile can be followed by a device in the missile which reacts to some property of the earth, such as magnetic or gravitational effects.

GUIDED MISSILE—An unmanned vehicle moving above the earth's surface, whose trajectory or flight path is capable of being altered by a mechanism within the vehicle. Following are some types of guided missiles (preceded by their basic designations, in which the first letter designates the origin of the missile and the second letter designates the objective):

AAM—Air-to-Air Missile
ASM—Air-to-Surface Missile
AUM—Air-to-Underwater Missile
SAM—Surface-to-Air Missile
SSM—Surface-to-Surface Missile
SUM—Surface-to-Underwater Missile
UAM—Underwater-to-Air Missile
USM—Underwater-to-Surface Missile

GYROSCOPE—A device consisting of a wheel so mounted that its spinning axis is free to rotate about either of two other axes perpendicular to itself and to each other; also the wheel of this device. (The characteristic of a gyroscope to maintain equilibrium makes it a useful component for many aircraft instruments.)

HARD BASE—Launching base that is protected against a nuclear bomb by a structure or terrestrial cover (natural or manmade tunnel); the structures are designed for a specified amount of overpressure.

HOLD—A pause in the launching or testing sequence or countdown of a missile or space vehicle. Pauses may be scheduled (i.e., to meet scheduled liftoff time) or unscheduled (i.e., weather, equipment malfunction).

HYPERSONIC—Speeds faster than Mach 5.

ICBM—Abbreviation for Intercontinental Ballistic Missile. ICBM range is normally considered 5,000 miles or more. (The ATLAS and TITAN are designated ICBM's.)

IGNITER—A device used to initiate burning of a fuel mixture of a propellant in a ramjet or rocket combustion chamber.

IGNITION—The initiation of combustion of a rocket motor. During the ignition phase, a supporting flame is maintained and a low flow rate of primary propellants

is begun. As soon as the propellants are burning properly, either an automatic or manual changeover to maximum performance burning is begun.

IM—Abbreviation for Interceptor Missile.

IMPACT PREDICTOR—A system which predicts the exact area in which a missile would impact during powered flight if its engine thrust were terminated. The impact predictor at Cape Canaveral is composed of three principal elements: (1) the AZUSA tracking system, (2) an IBM 709 highspeed digital computer, and (3) a plotting board in the Cape Central Control building. Position data received by the AZUSA are automatically relayed to the computer. The computer's output is relayed by cable to a plotting board monitored by the Range Safety Officer in Central Control. If it appears the missile might approach an unsafe area, the flight is terminated.

INSPECTION AND REPAIR AS NECESSARY (IRAN)—A term used to identify the maintenance work under which depot-level activities inspect and repair as necessary, as contrasted with complete disassembly and overhaul.

INTEGRATED WEAPON SYSTEM TRAINING (IWST)—The consolidated instructional period wherein personnel qualified in their respective specialties are trained to perform simultaneous and sequential duties and tasks involved in the accomplishment of an assigned operation or set of related operations. Detailed instruction is given all members of a team in performing required time-phased sequential duties and tasks.

INTEGRATING CONTRACTOR—A contractor to the Air Force, usually an associate contractor, to whom the Air Force has assigned the additional task of resolving interface considerations to insure proper operation and timely development of the complete Weapon System.

INTERFACE—(In an equipment sense.) A common boundary between two or more items of equipment. May be mechanical such as the physical surfaces and spacings in the mating of several parts, modules, components or subsystems, or electrical such as the matching of signal levels, impedances, power levels of two or more subsystems.

INTERFERENCE—1. In radio communication, the disturbance of reception owing to stray or undesired signals. 2. In radar, confusing signals accidentally produced on the indicator by the effect of either friendly or enemy electrical apparatus or machinery or by atmospheric phenomena.

INTERFERENCE CONTROL—The monitoring of radio frequencies assigned to a missile range for detection of interfering signals that could result in malfunctioning of missile-borne equipment, and the concerted effort to locate and terminate the source of interfering radiations.

IOC—"Initial operational capability."

IONOSPHERE—That portion of the earth's atmosphere, beginning about 30 miles above the earth's surface, which consists of layers of highly ionized air capable of bending or reflecting certain radio waves back to the earth. (This condition enables the transmission and reception of radio-frequency signals between two distant points.)

IRBM—Abbreviation for Intermediate

Range Ballistic Missile. IRBM range is usually considered about 1,500 miles. (The THOR, JUPITER, and POLARIS are designated IRBM's.)

JET—The exhaust stream or rapid flow of fluid from a small opening or nozzle.

JET VANE—A vane made of some highly heat-resisting material (e.g., graphite) placed in the jet stream for use in guidance of a missile.

JPL—Abbreviation for Jet Propulsion Laboratory (of the California Institute of Technology).

JUPITER—The surface-to-surface IRBM developed by the Army Ballistic Missile Agency and manufactured by Chrysler Corporation.

JUPITER-C—The four-stage Army rocket (elongated Redstone booster plus three solid propellant stages) used to launch Explorer No. 1, the first U.S. earth satellite.

LAUNCH—The initial motion in transition from static repose to dynamic flight. The moment when the missile is no longer supported by the launcher. The take-off. See LIFTOFF.

LAUNCH PAD—A concrete or other hard surface area on which a missile launcher is positioned.

LAUNCHER—A mechanical device, either mobile or stationary, which rigidly "cradles" or supports a missile in its proper launching position until the missile is launched. It directs the missile in the desired direction of flight during initial motion, but does not itself propel the missile.

LAUNCHER, ZERO LENGTH—A specially designed launcher, usually slightly longer than the missile it supports, which

can be adjusted, both in elevation and angle, so that missile heading can be controlled at take-off. Used primarily for cruise or aerodynamic type missiles, it is ideally suited for tactical launchings on land and also aboard ships.

LAUNCH COMPLEX—A general term intended to include all support facilities within a confined area which are vital to missile preflight check-out and launching. The combination of blockhouse, launch pad, and nearby supporting facilities are referred to as a "launch complex," since they are all contained within a relatively small area and all support the ultimate launching.

LAUNCHING OFFICER—The official having test control over the launching of a missile or research vehicle.

LIFTOFF—Initial movement of a ballistic missile or space vehicle as its rocket propulsion raises it from the launcher. (When applied to aerodynamic, or cruise missiles, this action is known as the "take-off.")

LIQUID PROPELLANT—Any liquid ingredient fed to the combustion chamber of a rocket engine.

LOGBALNET—An Air Material Command network for the exclusive use of transmitting ballistic missiles logistical data via electrical media. This includes both ICBM and IRBM.

LOX—Abbreviation for liquid oxygen. Used as a common oxidizer in liquid propellant rocket engines, it is oxygen supercooled so that its physical state is liquid.

MAIN STAGE—In the ignition sequence of a liquid propellant rocket, full thrust burning cannot be attempted immediately. In the early rocket motors the ignition began with an electrically ignited squib around which a small amount of propellant was allowed to pass. After ignition of the first propellant, a second step called primary stage burning was entered. In this step both propellants at limited flow rates were ejected into the combustion chamber. When burning appeared normal to a visual observer, a command would be given for full thrust, or so called main stage burning. This was the full thrust level burning which would result in lift-off of the rocket.

MAINTENANCE—All action taken to retain material in a serviceable condition or to restore it to serviceability. It includes inspection, testing, servicing, classification as to serviceability, repair, rebuilding, and reclamation.

MAJOR SUBSYSTEM—The major functional part of a weapon system which is essential to operational completeness. Examples are: Airframe, propulsion, armament, guidance, and communications.

"MAKE AND BUY" STRUCTURE—A composite listing of major parts and/or assemblies of an end item depicting those parts and/or assemblies which will be made on-site and off-site in addition to research and development studies conducted in support thereof. Details of each "MAKE AND BUY" STRUCTURE vary depending upon the complexity of the end item being considered and are negotiated on an individual basis.

MATADOR—An Air Force surface-to-surface missile produced by Martin, and used by the Tactical Air Command. A tactical cruise missile, it is known as the TM-61. It is the Air Force's first surface-to-surface missile.

MILESTONE—(In the programming sense.) A significant and frequently critical event having qualitative and/or quantitative aspects which, when completed, indicates the accomplishment of a step in progress toward a broader, planned goal.

MILITARY CHARACTERISTICS—Those characteristics of equipment upon which depend its ability to perform desired military functions. Military characteristics include physical and operational characteristics but not technical characteristics.

MINITRACK—The radio system used to track U.S. earth satellites. Originally developed at the Naval Research Laboratory as a part of Project VANGUARD, the system employs a low-power, lightweight transmitter in the satellite itself sending data (via radio waves) to several ground receiving stations.

MIXED FORCE—Concept of maintaining operational ballistic missiles and operational combat aircraft in the U.S. Air Force as a major deterrent to aggression.

MODIFICATION—The physical alteration of a system, subsystem, or equipment to change its designed capabilities or characteristics. Any change, correction in equipment structures, arrangement, or accessories affecting capabilities or characteristics.

MODULE—A combination of components, contained in one package or so arranged that together they are common to one mounting, which provide a complete function or functions to the subsystems and/or systems in which they operate. Sometimes called BLACK BOX, a vernacular term which should not be used.

NOSE CONE—Assembly at the forward end of a missile (or rocket vehicle) from which it is separated at the end of propelled flight. (In a research space vehicle, the nose cone contains the satellite and instrumentation equipment; in a military missile, the nose cone carries the warhead.)

Lockheed Missiles and Space Division

SATELLITE TEST CONTROL—At l. in foreground is Maj. V. H. Webb, controller at AF Satellite Test Center, from where all experimental satellites in polar orbit are controlled. Recovery of instrument capsules ejected from Discoverer series of satellites is supervised from this center. Tracking and communications are almost instant over millions of miles.

STATIC DISPLAY—At r. is a console that displays on closed-circuit TV the movement of weather systems over Pacific Ocean, so that the controllers can know when conditions are right for the recovery of satellite capsules. Display is called static because charts are made periodically and placed before TV cameras. There is no dynamic motion to any of the viewers.

OCEAN RANGE VESSEL—Former cargo ships modified with instrumentation equipment to gather performance data on missiles and rockets tested over the Atlantic Missile Range. Virtual "floating range stations," 11 of these vessels are used to bridge the long distances between islands on the far end of the range. They may also be used to extend the range to better than 6,000 miles. (See ATLANTIC MISSILE RANGE, above.)

OFFICE OF COORDINATING RESPONSIBILITY (OCR)—The office of coordinating responsibility (OCR) for a mission segment is that lowest echelon agency charged with giving support by technical or administrative advice, assistance and recommendations to the office of primary responsibility (OPR), to further the accomplishment of the mission segment.

OFFICE OF PRIMARY RESPONSIBILITY (OPR)—The office of primary responsibility (OPR) for a mission segment is that lowest echelon agency charged by its next higher echelon in the chain of command with the responsibility and authority for the accomplishment of the mission segment.

OPERATIONAL CHARACTERISTICS—Those military characteristics which pertain primarily to the functions to be performed by equipment, either along or in conjunction with other equipment, e.g., for electronic equipment, operational characteristics include such items as frequency coverage; channeling, type of modulation, and character of emission.

OPERATIONAL EVALUATION—The test and analysis of a specific end item or system, insofar as practicable under service operating conditions, in order to determine if quantity production is warranted considering (1) the increase in military effectiveness to be gained, and (2) its effectiveness as compared with currently available items or systems, consideration being given to (a) personnel capabilities to maintain and operate the equipment, (b) size, weight, and location considerations and (c) enemy capabilities.

OPERATIONAL MISSILE—A missile that, in contrast to a research and development missile, can be used to attack an enemy target.

ORBIT—The path in which a celestial body revolves about another body, as a planet moves about the sun or an artificial satellite about the earth.

ORBITAL VELOCITY—The velocity required to keep an object moving in a closed orbit around the sun, planet, or other celestial body. Orbital velocity of the earth is 18,000 mph.

OVERHAUL—The disassembly, cleaning, inspection, rework or replacement of parts or components, reassembly, adjustment and test of any item or accessory in accordance with applicable technical orders.

PACIFIC MISSILE RANGE—The instrumented range used by the Air Force Ballistic Missile Division for tracking missiles that extends many thousands of miles from Vandenberg Air Force Base, California, southward down the Pacific Ocean. Similar to the **ATLANTIC MISSILE RANGE** only in the sense that optical and radio tracking devices are placed along the range on islands and aboard ships, the PMR's mission is operational testing of missile weapon systems and satellite research.

PAD—A permanent or semipermanent load-bearing surface constructed or designed as a base upon which a launcher can be placed. Short for LAUNCH PAD.

PAD CHIEF—The individual charged with coordinating overall operations on the pad.

PAD SAFETY OFFICER—The individual responsible for maintaining safety practices during the launching operation. This includes such areas as fueling, arming of destruct packages, etc.

PART—The least subdivision of a system;

AF Ballistic Missile Division

an individual piece having an inherent functional capability but unable to function without the interaction of other parts or forces and ordinarily not subject to disassembly without destruction.

PAYLOAD—In a missile, the warhead, fuse and container. In research and test vehicles, this includes equipment for taking data and transmitting (or otherwise recovering) it.

PERIGEE—That point in an orbit nearest the earth. It is the opposite of apogee, or point in an orbit farthest from the earth.

PHYSICAL CHARACTERISTICS—Those characteristics of equipment which are primarily physical in nature, such as weight, shape, volume, waterproofing, and sturdiness.

POLARIS—The Navy's Fleet Ballistic Missile. It is a solid-propellant IRBM designed to be launched from a submarine or surface ship. Prime contractor is Lockheed.

PRELAUNCH TESTS—Tests of missile and/or ground equipment to determine readiness to launch. May include a countdown and a flight readiness firing with all launch complex equipment operating, but not including actual launching of the missile.

PREVENTIVE MAINTENANCE—The care and servicing by personnel for the purpose of maintaining equipment and facilities in satisfactory operating condition by providing for systematic inspection, detection, and correction of incipient failures either before they occur or before they develop into major defects.

PRIME CONTRACTOR—A contractor who enters into a contract with the Air Force.

PROCUREMENT LEAD TIME—The time elapsing between the initiation of procurement action and the receipt into the system of materiel purchased as a result of such actions. Procurement lead time is applicable to materiel to be obtained from any source outside the procuring department or by manufacture within that department and it is composed of three distinct elements:

1. The time elapsing between the initiation of procurement action and letting of contract or placing of order.
2. The time elapsing between letting of contract or placing of order and completion of manufacture.
3. The time elapsing between completion of manufacture and receipt of materiel into the system.

PRODUCTION—The process of making raw materials available and converting them by fabrication into required components and end items. It includes production functions of scheduling, inspection, inventory control, etc.

PRODUCT SUPPORT PERSONNEL—Includes those direct labor personnel in-

TEST CONTROL ROOM—From here, satellite controllers can watch both static and dynamic displays giving the position of test-satellites at key points of their orbits, movement of weather in relationship to positions and interrogation of the space-vehicles by tracking stations from Alaska and New Hampshire to Hawaii. An even more elaborate test control room is now being built.

Lockheed Missiles and Space Division

TIROS—A satellite to analyze weather movements by photographing earth's cloud shapes, coverage.

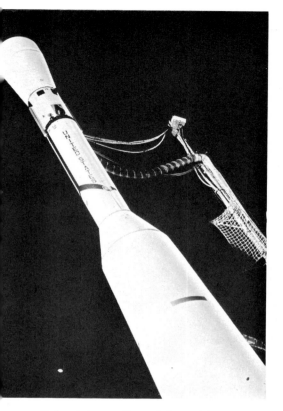

National Aeronautics and Space Administration

volved in service engineering, overhaul, storage, receipt, packaging, and reshipment of equipment that has been returned by operational units or personnel at test sites. The indirect labor portion includes the personnel involved in these areas but not involved in the actual overhaul or supply functions.

PROGRAM—In missile guidance, the planned flight events to be followed by the missile. The program includes all steps of the missile's guidance scheme and internal operations necessary to accomplish the desired objective. It is a schedule according to time of significant events planned to occur during the flight.

PROGRAMMED TURN—The turn of a ballistic missile from vertical motion, after liftoff, to a curved path approximating the desired powered flight trajectory prior to the initiation of guidance. Control signals are normally provided by a device in which nominal values for thrust, propellant mass flow, specific impulse, aerodynamic loads,

winds, and other trajectory disturbing influences are mechanized. Correction for off-nominal performance is not provided.

PROPAGATION—A term in the missile business to describe the manner in which an electromagnetic wave, such as a radar signal, timing signal or ray of light, travels from one point to another.

PROPELLANT—Any energy yielding material used to drive a vehicle. It may be either in liquid or solid form. If liquid, it may consist of one or more materials (although it generally contains two: *fuel* and the *oxidizer*).

PULSEJET—A jet-propulsion engine, containing neither compressor nor turbine, which produces thrust intermittently. Equipped with vanes in the front end which open and shut, it takes in air to create power in rapid periodic bursts rather than continuously. The German V-1 motor was of this type.

R & D—Research and Development.

RADAR—An electronic device which transmits bursts of radio energy and receives reflections of that energy from objects. The time consumed in this transmission-reflection cycle is accurately measured and converted to distance (range) from the radar to the objects. The highly directional nature of radar beams enables an accurate determination of direction to the object from the radar. The distance and direction information is presented on instruments allowing an operator to accurately locate the object in space. The word was derived from a contraction of the phrase, "*R*Adio *D*irection *a*nd *R*anging."

RAMJET—A type of jet engine consisting essentially of a tube open at both ends in which fuel is burned continuously to create a jet thrust, and having neither a compressor nor turbine, the air for oxidizing the fuel being rammed into the engine.

RANGE SAFETY OFFICER—An Air Force officer at the Atlantic or Pacific Missile Ranges charged with insuring that no missile presents a hazard or violates an unsafe area. He must insure that no missile impacts on the mainland or on inhabited down-range land areas.

REACTION TIME—The time interval between the command and actual launch.

RECLAMATION—The act or process of recovering serviceable and economically repairable equipment, components, and other materiel out of damaged, unserviceable, and excess material. (RECLAMATION includes inspection, classification, disassembly, cleaning, handling, and shipping. It is not ordinarily construed to include repairing.)

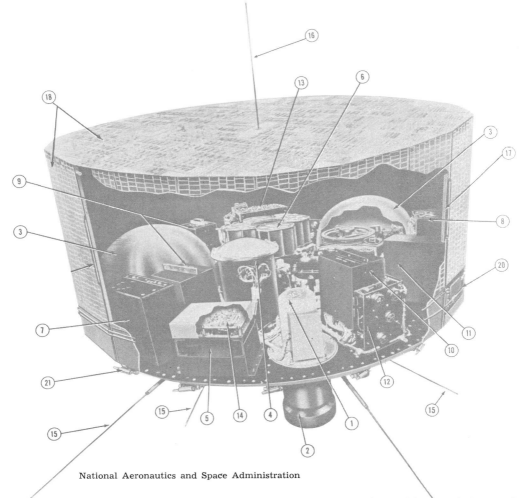

National Aeronautics and Space Administration

TIROS SATELLITE—Has two TV cameras, takes still pictures of earth's cloud cover (photos on facing page) and transmits them to ground stations. Tiros was designed and constructed by RCA, supervised by the U.S. Army Research and Development Laboratory. Photo keys: 1. One of two half-inch Vidicon TV cameras; 2. Wide-angle camera lens; 3. Tape recorders; 4. Electronic timer for operational sequencing; 5. TV transmitter; 6. Chemical batteries; 7. TV transmitter; 8. Recorder electronics; 9. Control circuits; 10. Auxiliary controls; 11. Power converter for tape motor; 12. Voltage regulator; 13. Battery charging regulator; 14. Auxiliary TV synchronizing generator; 15. Transmitting antennas; 16. Receiving antenna; 17. Sensor to measure position with respect to sun; 18. Solar cells; 20. De-spin device; 21. Spin-up rockets.

RECONDITIONING (COMPLETE)—Denotes all operations necessary to restore an item of weapon system equipment rendered unserviceable through fair wear and tear to a condition of complete operational serviceability. This RECONDITIONING includes compliance with all applicable technical directives, complete disassembly, necessary rework, subassembly, final assembly, adjustment and test.

RECOVERABLE—Means an item which can normally be returned to serviceable condition through maintenance.

RECOVERY—The act of retrieving a portion of a launched missile or satellite which has survived RE-ENTRY.

RE-ENTRY VEHICLE—A ballistic missile subsystem which was originally called the "nose cone." It normally is understood to include a heat shield, a warhead, an arming and fusing system, a re-entry attitude control system when necessary, and some device for separation of the re-entry vehicle from the main missile structure.

RECYCLE—To reschedule the countdown time back to an earlier phase of the count.

REDSTONE—An Army surface-to-surface missile with a 200-mile range, developed by the Army Ballistic Missile Agency and produced by Chrysler Corporation. The REDSTONE is deployed in support of our forces in Europe.

RESEARCH—A process of scientific investigation prior to and during development. It has for its aim the discovery of new scientific facts, techniques, and natural laws; an extension of the "state-of-the-art."

RESEARCH, APPLIED—Research aimed at specific application of scientific laws, principles, and phenomena. In contrast to basic research, the prospect of practical application of the results is a primary motive for applied research. Frequently even the methods to be used are clear before work is begun.

RESEARCH, BASIC—The theoretical or experimental study directed toward the increase of knowledge. It may result in the discovery of new scientific phenomena, principles, techniques, or significant data which add to the store of scientific knowledge. Immediate practical application is not necessarily a direct objective.

ROCKET—A thrust-producing system, or a complete missile, which derives its thrust from ejection of hot gases generated from material carried in the system, not requiring intake of air or water. (Rockets may be either of liquid or solid propellants.

SATELLITE—An unpowered object in space which revolves about another body.

SCIENTIFIC AND ENGINEERING PERSONNEL—Those persons engaged in scientific or technical duties which require formal education or its equivalent, such as aerodynamicists, physicists, chemists, electrical engineers, mathematicians, mechanical engineers, metallurgists, thermodynamicists, etc.

SCRUB—Missile jargon for the act of canceling a scheduled launch.

SECOR—An electronic tracking system employing several ground stations and a transponder in the missile to measure positions of the missile in flight.

SEPARATION—Regarding multistage missiles, the time or place at which a burnout stage is discarded and the remaining missile continues on its way.

SEQUENCER—A timing device which starts and stops instrumentation equipment according to a preset timed schedule. It may also be used to automatically control missile preflight operations and checkouts of the "countdown."

SHOPS AND PRODUCTION PERSONNEL—Includes those persons engaged in fabrication, assembly, test, checkout, acceptance, and other manufacturing operations. The other manufacturing operations referred to would include such things as flashing, annealing, heat treating, baking, refrigeration, anodizing, plating, painting and packaging. The manufacturing support functions of tooling and tool manufacturing are also to be included.

SHUTDOWN—Same as CUTOFF.

SKY SCREEN—An element of equipment used by the Range Safety Officer. The sky screen (either electronic or optical) provides a positive indication to the Range Safety Officer whenever the missile deviates from its planned trajectory. In operational use, one sky screen is used to monitor flight azimuth, and another is used to monitor vertical programming.

SM—Abbreviation for Strategic Missile.

SNARK—An Air Force surface-to-surface intercontinental air-breathing cruise missile used by the Strategic Air Command. Developed by Northrop, it is also called the SM-62.

SOFT BASE—An installation on which

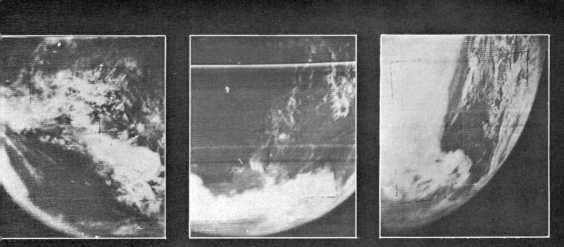

UMBILICAL CABLES—Wire connecting electronic components of a missile with instruments and electronic computers in control room of a block-house or underground launch-silo. Cables disconnect as missile lifts off its pad. At l., tower with cables is shown at moment of disconnect. Above, symbolically, is portrait of Lt. General Bernard Schriever, Commander of the Air Force Systems Command, the AF man most responsible for success of ICBMs. Missile shown is IRBM Thor, modified with Able 2nd stage for space research.

AF Missile Test Center

facilities are functionally designed to accomplish an assigned mission without being constructed to resist overpressure, heat, radiation, penetration of other weapon effects to be anticipated under enemy attack.

SONIC—Of or pertaining to sound, especially, in aviation contexts, to the speed of sound. (Sound travels at different speeds through different mediums, and it travels at different speeds under different conditions of temperature, etc. In air under standard sea-level conditions, sound travels at approximately 1,100 feet per second, or 750 mph.)

SQUIB—A small pyrotechnic device which may be used to fire the igniter in a rocket or for some similar purpose. Not to be confused with a detonator which explodes.

STRATOSPHERE—A calm region of the upper atmosphere characterized by little or no temperature change with a change in altitude. The stratosphere is separated from the lower atmosphere, or troposphere, by the tropopause. An important part of the stratosphere is ozone, which plays a vital role in the phenomenon of selective absorption, and seems to have a significant correlation with surface weather conditions. The stratosphere is free from the clouds and convective currents of the troposphere.

S.R.O.—The abbreviation for Superintendent of Range Operations. He is the overall director and coordinator for the Range during a launching operation, and coordinates activity in the Operations Room of Central Control at the Cape Canaveral Missile Test Annex.

STATIC FIRING—The testing of all operating functions of a missile, including ignition and run up of the propulsion stages, while the missile is tied down to its test stand.

STATIC TESTS—Ground tests intended to investigate the structural integrity of a missile. Sometimes used as synonymous with CAPTIVE TEST.

SUBASSEMBLY—A combination of parts comprising a definable entity of a component and performing a function essential to the proper operation of that component.

SUBCONTRACT—Any purchase order or other contractual instrument or commitment entered into by a prime contractor or subcontractor with parties other than the Government.

SUBSYSTEM—A single module, or a combination of modules, plus independent components that contribute to modular functions, all interconnected and interrelated within a system and performing a specific system function.

SUPERSONIC—Faster than sonic speed, or the speed of sound.

SUPPORT SYSTEM—A composite of equipment, skills, and techniques which, while not an instrument of combat, has the function of performing a clearly defined function in support of an Air Force mission.

SURVEILLANCE—The operations of visual and radar searching from aircraft, ground and ship stations to determine that the Range is free of shipping, other aircraft traffic, etc., and that safe conditions exist to permit missile launching. Also, the subsequent act of keeping the missile itself (as well as the Range) under the watchful eye of the Range Safety Officer, through optical or electronic means, to assure that the missile travels its prescribed course or is destroyed.

TECHNICAL CHARACTERISTICS—Those characteristics of equipment which pertain primarily to the engineering principles involved in producing equipment possessing desired military characteristics, e.g., for electronic equipment, technical characteristics include such items as circuitry, and types and arrangements of components.

TECHNICAL EVALUATION—The study and investigations by a developing agency to determine the technical suitability of material, equipment, or a system, for use in the military services.

TELEMETERING SYSTEM—A method of taking measured values within the missile and transmitting these values electronically to a ground station. The information received at the ground station can be used to evaluate the internal performance of a missile in flight.

TELEMETRY—Telemetry is the radio link between a missile and the ground station used to transmit information described (above) under telemetering system.

TERM CONCEPT—(In Contracting.) In a contract written on a "term" basis, the contractor agrees to make available facilities, material and personnel, and to furnish an estimated number of man-years, man-months, or man-hours of scientific effort for a stated period of time directed toward the accomplishment of the required research and development program.

TEST VEHICLE—A rocket or jet powered craft used in testing components of proposed missile systems.

THEODOLITE—Basically, an accurate surveyor's transit. On the range a conventional transit or theodolite is ill adapted to recording missile position during flight. Accordingly, the theodolites for range use have evolved into cine-theodolites (see ASKANIA) and photo-theodolites. The latter differ from cine-theodolites in that the cine camera is replaced by a precision, fixed (glass) plate camera in which a large field is viewed and multiple exposures are made on the arc plate of the missile as it moves through the field of view. Whereas a cine-theodolite is a tracking instrument, the photo-theodolite is locked in position during the photographic recordings.

THOR—An Air Force strategic weapon now on operational duty with the RAF in the United Kingdom. Also called SM-75.

THROAT—In rocket and jet engines, the most constricted section of an exhaust nozzle. At the throat gas flow velocities (for supersonic flow rates) always equal sonic velocity. After the throat, the nozzle expands and flow velocities increase to supersonic values.

THRUST—The driving force exerted on a rocket or missile by its jet or rocket engine or engines, or other propulsive force.

THRUST DECAY—When a rocket motor burns out or is cut off, propulsive thrust does not fall to zero instantaneously, but progressively declines over some fraction of a second. This graduated reduction and loss of thrust is known as "thrust decay."

TITAN—An Air Force surface-to-surface ICBM produced by the Martin Co. Also known as the SM-68.

TM—Abbreviation for Tactical Missile.

TRAJECTORY—The path of a missile or space vehicle as it moves in space, from the time it leaves its launcher to completion of its flight.

X-17 RESEARCH ROCKET—At r., a 3-stage vehicle using solid propellants to probe hypersonic speeds.

VERNIER ROCKET—Small rockets that are fired for stability and control of a big rocket airframe.

AF Missile Test Center

Lockheed Missiles and Space Division

TRANSPONDER—An electronic device that receives a challenging signal and automatically transmits a response. The transponder consists of a receiver, which receives the signal impulses, and a responder (or transmitter) that returns signal impulses to the interrogator-responser (e.g., DOVAP).

TROPOPAUSE—The boundary or transition zone between the troposphere and the stratosphere.

TROPOSPHERE—The lower layer of the earth's atmosphere, extending from the surface of the earth to an altitude of ten miles. Although the composition of the air remains more or less constant, its density decreases rather rapidly with altitude; 75% of the atmosphere's weight is found in the troposphere.

T-TIME—The time of liftoff (or take-off) of a missile from its launch pad.

TUMBLING—An unsatisfactory attitude situation in which the vehicle continues on its flight, but turns end-over-end about its center of gravity with its longitudinal axis remaining in the plane of flight.

TURBOJET—A jet motor whose air is supplied by a turbine-driven compressor, the turbine being activated by exhaust gases from the motor.

UMBILICAL CORD—A cable fitted to the missile with a quick disconnect plug, through which missile equipment is controlled and tested while the vehicle is still attached to launching equipment. The umbilical cord is detached at or just prior to liftoff of the missile.

VENTURI TUBE—A short tube with varying cross sections and a constricted throat. Flow through the tube causes an increase in flow velocity at the throat which, in turn, results in diminished pressure within the fluid at the throat. The venturi tube is used in measuring airspeed, and advantage has been taken of the diminished pressure at the throat to operate a gyroscope or other device.

VERNIER—A rocket engine of small thrust used in a ballistic missile to control the roll, pitch, and yaw attitudes during propelled flight and to make the final adjustment of the missile's velocity and trajectory just after the thrust of the final stage main engines has been cut off.

WARHEAD—Normally, that part of a missile containing an explosive, chemical, or other charge intended to damage the enemy. However, warheads of missiles being tested at AFMTC contain no explosives or other lethal charges. Instead, this section of the vehicle is devoted completely to instrumentation equipment (for recording performance of the missile under test).

WEAPON SYSTEM—Equipment, skills, and techniques, the composite of which forms an instrument of combat. The complete WEAPON SYSTEM includes all related equipment, materiel, services, and personnel required solely for the operation of the air vehicle, or other major element of the system, so that the instrument of combat becomes a self-sufficient unit of striking power in its intended operational environment.

X-17—A three-stage ballistic test vehicle, developed by Lockheed, for collecting data to be applied in the ICBM and IRBM development programs. (The Army, Navy, and Air Force have found information collected by the X-17 useful in their respective ballistic missile programs. Most notable contribution of the X-17 was its role in perfecting ICBM re-entry nose-cones.) •

warpower for peace:
MISSILES

These powerful, destructive weapons were planned to keep peace by discouraging war and have paid off in progress, a better life.

TO THE average American, I am sure, a missile has become the symbol of violent destruction and death. In point of fact, missiles are conceived and developed to destroy specific kinds of targets. Their function in this respect—and the need for them—is explained in other chapters of this book, those chapters that deal with strategic, tactical and defense weapon systems. Without an arsenal of such systems, the Free World would be in grave danger indeed—whether the uneasy peace of a cold war prevails or a tragic hot war is started by our enemies in that "curtained off" portion of the world that is not free. But something not quite so evident to the average American, I am equally sure, is the real symbolism that missiles have created by their superb performance in the service of scientific research.

A missile today has become a true symbol of progress, peace and a better life for the human race.

How can this be so? In a most elementary way, missiles preserve world peace. The more versatile and powerful is the Free World's missile arsenal, the less probability there is that an enemy would care to chance having his nation or military forces devastated. There is a critical point of punishment beyond which no nation could survive economically or physically. The point varies, of course, with the nation. It is the aim of the United States to build an arsenal of versatile missiles in such magnitude that *all* enemies will be discouraged, now and in the future, from starting a war.

In a less obvious way, missiles have become the symbol of progress and a better life. In the process of their development, modern technology in a decade has gained more new knowledge and facilities than it had acquired for a half-century before missiles appeared on the scene. Developments in electronics alone bear this out. Plastics is another example. There are few fields of technology that missile design and production have not stimulated. New techniques acquired in these fields are applied to the manufacture of better and comparatively cheaper consumer goods. Better and safer automobiles, for example, have come out of research with rocket-powered sleds.

Even less obvious are the benefits that missiles have reaped for the future of the human race. Scientific research in outer space would have been impossible without missiles. The rocket engines and booster-stages of missiles have been modified to boost scientific instruments into orbit about the earth and the sun. Unsuspected new knowledge has been gained in this way. Scientists now have a much clearer picture of the mysterious forces that deeply affect the world's weather and life. This certainly will profit your future. •

Official USAF Photos, one below by Haynes

First reliable workhorse of the Space Age was the Thor strategic missile, built by Douglas Aircraft for the Air Force. The center photo pictures the complete weapon including warhead. All the others are modifications of it.

At r. is prelaunch view
of Thor with Able stage
on top. This 2-stage Thor
has performed remark-
able feats in space scientific research. Able stage
was perfected in launches
of Martin Co.'s Vanguard.

69

Below, Thor-Able rises toward regions of deep space from Launch Pad 17A at Cape Canaveral. Its payload was boosted by the rockets to almost 25,000 mph, thus breaking the grip of gravity.

Photo, Ed Thomas. Air Force Missile Test Center

Preliminary steps in mating a science-research 2nd stage to Thor missile are shown here. Able stage, built by Aerojet-General, is hauled into place high up on the gantry which services the towers by a cable.

Photos above and below are by DeFillips, from Air Force Missile Test Center

Gantry is then rolled on steel tracks to where Thor sits on launch pad. View here depicts Able stage being gently let down onto top of Thor, where it will sit in adapter-collar and be held in position by bolts.

At l., Able-Star 2nd stage is checked out with electronic and pressure instruments before being adapted to Thor booster. Able-Star, by Aerojet-General, was America's 1st rocket that could be stopped and restarted in space.

Thor-Able-Star sits ready for launch on Pad 17B at Cape Canaveral after the servicing gantry has been rolled away. It created technological history by successfully placing into orbit Transit 1B, a satellite for navigational aid sponsored by the Navy and the Defense Department.

USAF Photo, from Army Ballistic Missile Agency

Above is Jupiter C with Army's Explorer space "moon" in its nose instead of a destructive warhead. This missile sent America's first artificial satellite into orbit around the earth.

Vestby Photo. Air Force Missile Test Center

Directly above sits a modified Juno II with a NASA deep-space probe in place of warhead. Gantry work-platforms are being opened out so that the servicing tower can be rolled away.

At l., Jupiter missile is serviced before test flight. Compare this weapon with space-research modified version at top l., which was an earlier form of missile, based on Redstone.

USAF Photo, from Army Ballistic Missile Agency

On Dec. 18, 1958, the Air Force successfully launched its 1st satellite into orbit. At r., is shown the missile, an Atlas ICBM, that did the job. Compare this ICBM with other Atlases on this page.

Directly above, an Atlas ICBM, stands ready to cover intercontinental distances with its strategic warhead of thermonuclear type. Atlas is built by Convair-Astronautics Div. in San Diego, California.

At r., Atlas-Able waits for the moon to come into right position before servicing and launch. Unfortunately, this modified missile exploded on pad. But other tries will be made to orbit moon.

An Atlas-Able with Agena satellite system on top is shown at l. Atlas-Able-Agena combination has successfully launched into orbit from pole to pole both the SAMOS and MIDAS satellites.

At r., above, is scene of mating test capsule for Mercury Project in Atlas gantry. Capsule was successfully launched and recovered, as was later one carrying a live chimp who was boosted 150 miles into space and over 400 miles downrange. Chimp was recovered alive and in good health. Same day an Atlas boosted a SAMOS reconnaissance satellite into orbit (Feb. 1, 1961). Directly at r., Mercury capsule is trucked into pad area, escorted by Security Police.

Photo. McNearny Air Force Missile Test Center

At l., is Atlas with a Mercury capsule installed as servicing gantry pulls away. Below are two versions of Titan, an early test model (at l.) and the full 2-stage missile with warhead carrying thermonuclear blast. Although warhead carries test instruments in launch shown, first operational models with real thing aboard will be installed in underground silos shortly after this book appears, by summer 1961. Like Thor, the first dependable space research workhorse, Titan is almost sure to become the heavyweight dependable. A Titan-Agena B, now being considered, will be able to boost 4 tons in orbit or heavy pay loads to the moon and beyond.

USAF; Martin-Denver

Official USAF Photo. from The Martin Company

warpower for peace:
AIRCRAFT

Missiles and manned aircraft are not incompatible.
The combination protects the nation, aids science.

A POPULAR conception in this age of automatic missiles is that airplanes and the men needed to pilot them are no longer necessary. This attitude refers to military aircraft, of course, and not to the craft of commercial or private aviation. The myth has been encouraged from many sources—none of them very closely familiar with what goes on in the U. S. Air Force or the Naval Bureau of Aeronautics. In fact, ever since 1957—when the first sputnik flew into orbit—there has been talk that the USAF and Naval Air Arm were obsolete. One national magazine of multi-million circulation even flatly stated on its cover that the flying Air Force was done for. This is irresponsible and dangerous talk. It misleads the American public and weakens the defense posture of the Free World. It also hampers scientific progress in the fields of missiles and spaceflight—those very fields it purports to be championing. The flying Air Force and the flying Navy are far from being dead ducks. Without them, men of the Kremlin and Peiping would be stamping freely all over Europe and Asia. Without them, there would have been no background of knowledge in high-speed flight and air-frame design—just as necessary in developing a space ship as in designing a modern airplane. Each fragment of knowledge gained at an unknown frontier, rolls back that frontier just a little farther. Once the sound barrier to supersonic flight was an unknown quantity. The chapter on "Jets Behind the Scenes" describes how aerospace progress is made. Read it for a picture of how high-performance flying vehicles are developed, one from the other—and *ad infinitum* into the realm of space and beyond. On this page, at left, is the Navy's F-4D Sky Ray shown just as it knocked a radio-controlled drone aircraft out of the sky with a heat-seeking Sidewinder missile. Below is the Air Force's huge B-52 Stratofortress carrying Hound Dog air-to-ground missiles.

Except as noted, all illustrations in this chapter are Official USAF and Navy Photos

McDonnell Aircraft Corporation

Atop the facing page are four of the Navy's F8U Crusader jet aircraft, as they approach their carrier, the USS Forrestal far below, for a landing after completing a patrol mission for the Sixth Fleet in the Mediterranean. At page bottom are four Century-Series supersonic aircraft of the Air Force. Shown against the rugged mountains surrounding Edwards Air Force Base in California's Mojave Desert, where they were perfected by flight testing, these sophisticated flying machines provided a background of experience for their designers and manufacturers that led in almost a straight line to instrumentation and controls for research rockets and satellites. They are the McDonnell F-101 Voodoo (at top) and McDonnell now produces the manned capsule for the Mercury astronauts; the Convair F-102 Delta Dagger (out front) and Convair now produces the Atlas ICBM, scheduled to shoot the Mercury capsule into orbit; the Lockheed F-104 Starfighter (at rear) and Lockheed now produces the Agena rocket-satellite, which is making possible a variety of other satellites for reconnaissance, defense warning and intercept of enemy satellites; and finally, the first of the supersonic series, North American Aviation's F-100 Super Sabre (at bottom) and North American is now developing the B-70 Valkyrie, a chemical-powered bomber that can double as a space ship or satellite-booster. Atop this page is Republic Aviation's Thunderchief, a mighty tactical fighter–bomber. Republic is now going into the space business earnestly. Below the Thunderchief is a close-up view of the Voodoo.

79

The F-107 at left has only a number for its name. It's a double "mach-buster" designed and built by North American Aviation. A single-seat fighter that did not go into production, its major purpose was manned research at twice the speed of sound. Things learned during test program provided the National Aeronautics and Space Administration with valuable data for training space pilots. Directly below on this page is the Navy's F11F Tiger, built by Grumman. It can fly at more than 1,000 miles an hour and is shown with Sidewinder air-to-air missiles under its wings. An enemy aircraft cannot possibly escape these lethal missiles, which home-in on the infrared radiations from heat of a jet engine. Six Navy Sidewinders were tested by the Chinese Nationalists in the Battle of Formosa Straits. Every one of them flew up the tailpipe of a MIG-17 piloted by the Chinese Reds, destroying it. Across the bottom of these pages are two views of the Air Force F-106 Delta Dart, designed and built by Convair. Looking like an angry insect from another planet, the Dart is an interceptor used to defend the United States against enemy attack. It can fly 1,500 miles at twice the speed of sound, carrying the MB-1 Genie, a nuclear missile which in a single shot could destroy a fleet of enemy bombers.

On this page are pictured the Navy's A3D Skywarrior and the Air Force B-66 Destroyer. These were both designed by Douglas Aircraft, which makes the Thor ballistic missile, and are practically the same airplane. They are twin-jet tactical bombers that, with in-flight refueling, have considerable range and great striking force. The latest Air Force model has an automatic electrical control system that eliminates at least 10 pilot functions and requires no manual switching. Its development added knowledge that must pay off eventually in terms of the design of efficient navigation controls for space ships. The strip above showing tiny B-66 shapes between star-like forms is an actual sequence-photo made from an RB-66, the reconnaissance version of this bomber. The "stars" resulted from a new flare, developed at the Air Proving Ground, to make detailed nighttime reconnaissance photography possible. On the facing page, at top, is the Air Force B-58 Hustler, by Convair. Here is a delta-wing bomber that could fly around the world at Mach 2, with in-flight refueling, and devastate an enemy across continents with its nuclear-bomb payload. This kind of airplane makes a potential enemy of the Free World think hard several times before he starts shooting. The Air Force says officially that "the B-58 achieved a greater speed increase over the fastest previous strategic bomber than was reached in the preceding 50 years of aircraft design and manufacture." Below the B-58 is shown the Navy's newest attack bomber, the A2F-1 Intruder. The Intruder is the first Navy low-level attack bomber with an ability to deliver with great accuracy either nuclear or conventional weapons on targets completely obscured by bad weather or darkness. This is due to its sensitive electronic detection and firing devices. The Intruder was designed and built by the Grumman Aircraft Engineering Corporation.

Opposite is a manned airplane that looks more like a space ship than a space ship itself. This is the B-70 Valkyrie bomber that can fly beyond three times the speed of sound in regions of the atmosphere no other airplane could invade. Its size, power, bomb load and number of crew members are all classified top secret. Yet it could act as launching platform for a heavy space rocket in the higher reaches of the stratosphere, where the thin air resistance would increase the launched rocket's capability by many times. Quoting Lt. General Roscoe Wilson, Air Force Deputy Chief of Staff for Development: "While we need the brute power of ICBMs, they lack the flexibility essential to winning a military victory. We will continue to need manned aircraft to seek out hidden and mobile targets—to restrike residual targets and perform a variety of other tasks. We look forward to the B-70, which is now under development, as the essential partner of the ICBM." Only in this way can peace be maintained—if an enemy *knows* he can get away with . . . *nothing*. The B-52 Stratofortresses shown below may be subsonic, but they keep the peace on the same terms. •

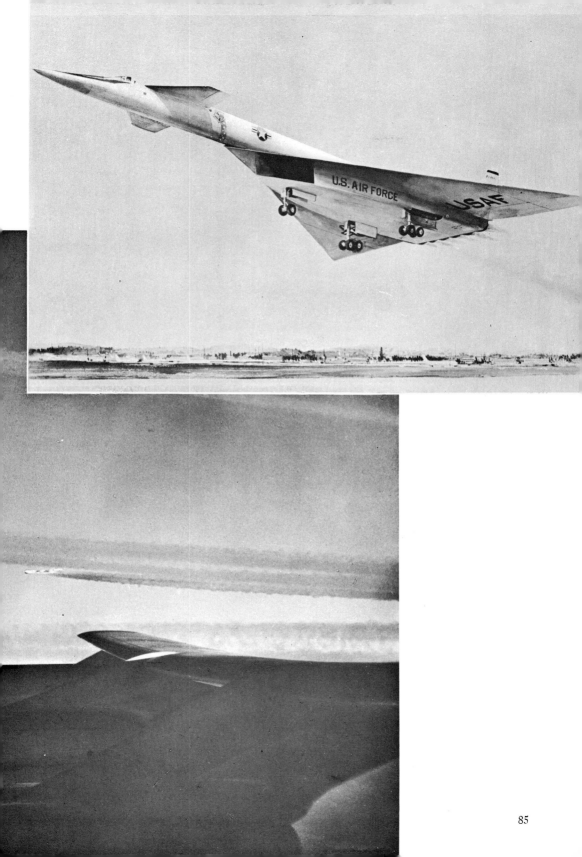

NUCLEO–EXOTIC PROPULSION

New engines, derived from subatomic physics, may even change the solar system.

Lockheed scientists envision trips to Mars/Venus during 1970s by combining liquid-fuel and nuclear rockets. Reactor glows on cable. Cutaway: Liquid tanks, fuel exhausted, transporting "cocooned" load.

Painting by Al Montgomery, Lockheed Missiles and Space Division

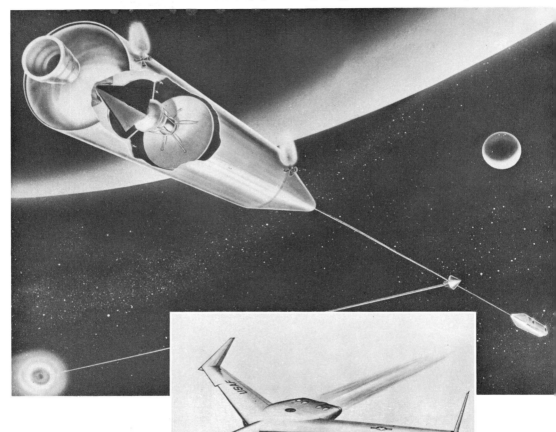

At right are two artist's concepts of ANP aircraft now being developed by Convair. ANP means "Aircraft Nuclear Propulsion." Aircraft are (top) powered by indirect liquid metal cycle and by direct air cycle method. Latter can use either a modified turbo-prop or a turbofan engine.

Official USAF Photos

AS World War II came to an end, the Scientific Advisory Board of the (then) U. S. Army Air Forces was established by a directive of that great visionary general officer, "Hap" Arnold. The purpose of the Board was to lay down a plan for building America's airpower through science to a position where it would tower above the air strength of all other nations in the world. General Hap Arnold's purpose was to assure the survival of democracy throughout the future. He felt that if the United States were never caught napping again—as we had been when Pearl Harbor and the Navy were paralyzed by a sneak air attack—that our air power strength alone could not only discourage the start of another war, but that it would also continually add new knowledge to the science of aeronautics.

A year later, in 1946, the Board presented their proposals to General Arnold. Among those proposals were two that raised eyebrows among less farsighted scientists than the Board members. One of these was a program for breaking the sound barrier. "The sonic barrier is a wall beyond which no airplane can fly," was the response of a majority of aeronautical scientists. Another proposal was the development of a missile that could fly across continents. The response to that is worth a separate paragraph of quotation.

"I say, technically, I don't think anybody in the world knows how to do such a thing, and I feel confident it will not be done for a very long period of time to come." This statement has been

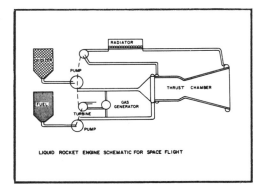

Schematic of typical chemical rocket engine here shows general simplicity, but it's quite wasteful of fuel and requires heavy tank loads for flight.

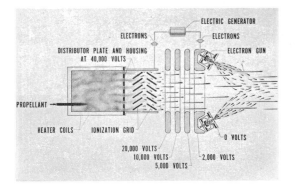

NASA's simplified diagram of ion engine shows high voltages needed to create and accelerate ions in steps. Power could be obtained from sun.

Diagrams: Rocketdyne Division, NAA, and NASA

Compare this typical ion propulsion system with schematic of chemical rocket system just above. It is more complex and demanding of engineers.

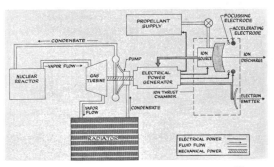

General Electric Co.'s ANP Dept. was first to operate a turbojet engine on nuclear power. Engine shown did job. It was modified from J-47 aircraft jet, first proved out by Martin Co. in XB-51 (see page 129).

Gunnar Thornton, manager of Design Engineering at GE's ANP Dept., explains to girls of his dept. how chemical combustion chamber of jet is replaced with reactor for direct air cycle engine.

credited to Dr. Vannevar Bush, Chief Scientist for the U. S. Government during World War II. He was unquestionably sincere in his attitude.

That was about 15 years ago, from the moment of my writing about it. Today, the Army Air Forces is a separate (and the largest) military department—the U. S. Air Force. Today, also, America has three different kinds of ICBM, for different purposes. The sound barrier has long ago proved to be no "wall" against supersonic flight.

Because of these achievements, and because I am very strongly convinced that no scientist—no matter how expert he may be in his special field—can say with certainty that *anything* is impossible or improbable of achievement, I have taken the liberty of coining a new expression for the title of this chapter. "Nucleo-Exotic Propulsion" covers the range of goals that had been considered impossible in the past to those that are even now considered fantastic. It includes the many "far-out" projects that presently are in development.

As an aside, it is interesting to recall the stand of Great Britain's Air Ministry regarding the turbojet aircraft engine. An engineer named Whittle proposed such an engine in 1930. The Air Ministry replied that "the practical difficulties were too great." Primarily because of this, it took more than another decade for Rolls-Royce to produce the Nene—the world's first aircraft jet engine.

The ICBMs previously mentioned were dependent basically upon two factors: 1, new propulsion systems and 2, new guidance systems. Eleven years ago, in 1950, propulsion systems for space flight were all but unknown. Few serious engineers or scientists wrote technical papers on such a subject in the near-past of a half-dozen years. Right now, however, in 1961, such technical papers jam the pages of scientific and engineering journals. Actual research projects of the military, the civilian Space Administration, at universities and in industry are well launched in the field of propulsion methods that can only be called "exotic," even by the people at work on them.

A decade ago, there were only the chem-

At left is test-reactor by name of "Susie," after the name of small daughter of a GE engineer on project. Also called a "pool-reactor," it is one of tools used to develop nuclear aircraft engines of practically limitless endurance and range. Reactor has 1 megawatt power, is sunk in 30-ft.-deep pool of water that acts as shield against radiation.

All photos on these facing pages are from the ANP Department, General Electric Company

The three photos here give some idea of nuclear fuel element compactness for aircraft. Above is tiny unit compared to lead pencil. Its rings contain uranium oxide. A series of such units make up a cartridge of only 13 lbs., as shown at right; its energy equals tons of jet fuel. Other, smaller fuel units are being developed, as demonstrated by pretty blonde above other pretty blonde, at right.

ical-powered rocket engines, using the equivalent of gunpowder for the solid propellant rockets and cryogenic or hypergolic fuels for the big engines. A rocket engine does not require air for combustion of its fuel. It carries its own atmosphere along with it—which is why it is today the only engine that can perform in airless space. Its atmosphere is the oxidizer, an equivalent of the oxygen that makes combustion possible within the earth's atmosphere. The most popular cryogenic oxidizer is liquid oxygen—which starts to boil at almost 300 degrees below zero Fahrenheit. This is the reference of cryogenic—extremely low in temperature. It can be seen that such oxidizers present difficulties in handling and storage. Hypergolic rocket fuels are self-igniting. As they meet in the combustion chamber, ignition is spontaneous. There is no need for an igniter, which makes the hypergolic fuels more reliable. The most popular oxidizers

for these fuels are Red or White Fuming Nitric Acid. Such oxidizers are highly corrosive and dangerous to handle.

It is a tribute to man's ingenuity and technology that out of such fuel-oxidizer combinations he has built machines which have sent satellites into orbit around the earth and the sun. It is an even greater tribute that he could use them to propel giant missiles across continents to strike targets with unbelievable accuracy. Dr. Vannevar Bush as much as said that such a feat was impossible. But already well along in the research and development phase are engines to make the others appear primitive indeed. These are cryptically called ANP and RNP systems.

The former is Aircraft Nuclear Propulsion and the latter, Rocket Nuclear Propulsion. These fields of propulsion technology are just as new today as the cryogenic and hypergolic propulsion fuels were a decade ago. Once nuclear propul-

GE ANP Dept. already has nuclear fuel elements on production-line status. To prevent radiation damage to employees, arm-length plastic gloves are mounted in shielded cases. Elements can be manipulated safely.

ANP Department, General Electric Company

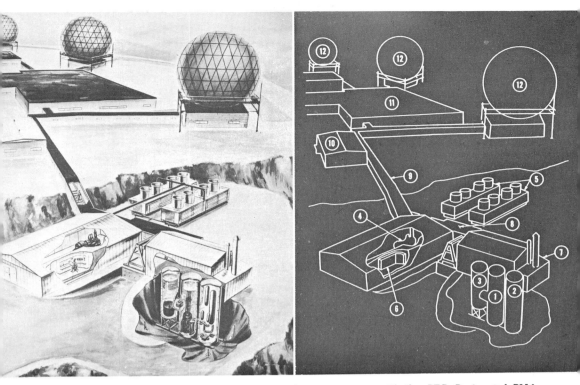

The Martin Co. has completed this nuclear power plant, on contract with the AEC. Designated PM-1 (Portable, Medium Power), it's built in prepackaged units for airlift, could be used on the moon. Diagram shows 1) reactor tank, 2) steam generator tank, 3) spent fuel storage tank, 4) steam turbine and electric generator, 5) air steam condensers, 6) control console, 7) shield water cooler, 8) decontamination/water chemistry lab, 9) walkway, 10) tech supply bldg., 11) base ops building, and 12) radar installations.

All illustrations on this page: The Martin Company, Baltimore-Nuclear Division

Martin-Nuclear has been highly successful in developing miniaturized nuclear power plants. Above is SNAP-3, midget generator. Fueled by radioisotopes, it has operated in vacuum at minus 100°, space conditions. Size of unit is seen above. Concept at right by Martin Artist Jack Riggin shows 2 SNAP-1A units on satellite. SNAP: "System for Nuclear Auxiliary Power."

Cloud chambers are used by NASA and others to learn more about basic actions of thermonuclear reactions. Here, cloud is alcohol vapor being bombarded by alpha particles (helium nuclei of high energy) created from source of polonium. Colliding particles of helium and alcohol are visible through vapor and give picture of energy interactions. Out of such research may come thermonuclear or plasma engines for future space rockets.

Except as noted, illustrations on these facing pages from National Aeronautics and Space Administration

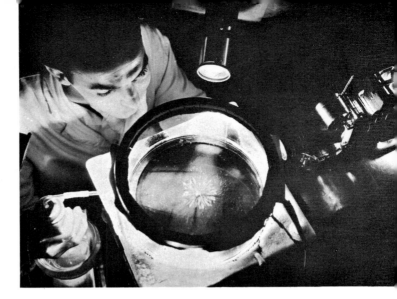

Schematic of nuclear fission rocket below would probably use Uranium 235 or polonium for source, as suggested by control rod, cleverly arranged. System combines thrust from turbine and rocket.

Rocketdyne Division, NAA

Much simplified thermonuclear plasma accelerator below suggests how H-bomb fusion might be controlled for propulsion. Hot electrical plasma for thrust has to be contained inside magnetic field.

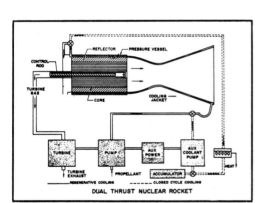

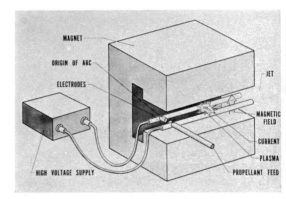

sion systems are perfected, the aerospace sciences will leap ahead with a speed that certainly must appear as remarkable, if not more so, as the swift progress made following the introduction of practical chemical rocket engines.

An example of the difference in efficiency between a nuclear rocket and the (now) conventional combination of liquid oxygen and kerosene is their specific impulse. This is a technical engineering term, but it simply means the amount of thrust obtained per second from a rocket engine for each pound of fuel burned. The specific impulse of the present conventional liquid rocket fuels is about 300 seconds— or 300 pounds of thrust per second for each pound of fuel that is burned up. It can

be seen easily that to obtain the great thrusts needed to hurl ICBMs like Atlas or Titan through space, a tremendous payload of fuel is required. The fuel-weight itself requires additional thrust to lift it off the ground, so the situation can be likened to a dog chasing his tail. On the other hand, the specific impulse of a nuclear rocket is from 900 to 1,000 seconds— or at least three times that of the operational liquid rockets of today!

With a nuclear rocket developing 1,000 pounds of thrust per second for each pound of fuel burned, it could boost extremely heavy scientific or military payloads through space on a minimum of fuel. This is at the other end of the spectrum from the solid-fuel rockets, which have re-

At right is actual photo of ion beam in vacuum tank, which simulates conditions of outer space. System to accelerate ions (positively charged atoms) is barely visible at left, but at right can be seen shock waves.

Below is chart showing a nuclear turboelectric type of rocket engine, indicating various kinds of energy sources. Charged particles are shot from nozzle by magnetic field, providing high-velocity rocket thrust.

Above photo from Rocketdyne Division, NAA

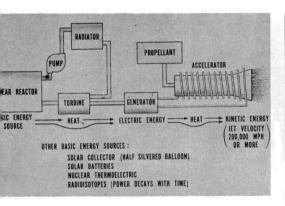

ceived so much publicity fanfare lately. A solid-propellant rocket engine has a quite low specific impulse. Present engines of this type can provide high thrust only for an extremely short burning time. This does not necessarily mean such a condition will persist. In the cases of missiles like Minuteman, Polaris and Pershing, techniques have been developed for shutting off solid-fuel engines with considerable accuracy in flight. One of the requirements for space missions is an ability to shut down the rocket engines after a predetermined, *precise* velocity is attained. Thus the solid-propellant engine may in the future prove feasible as a space booster. But as things now stand, lunar and interplanetary flight must depend on liquid-fuel rockets with

The Lewis Research Center of NASA is not content with small lab models alone to test electrical propulsion systems: here is big ion rocket tester. Specific impulse of ion rocket far exceeds nuclear.

nuclear-powered upper stages—for success.

The National Aeronautics and Space Administration (NASA) is experimenting with an advanced liquid-fuel combination —liquid oxygen and liquid hydrogen. The latter has an even lower boiling point than liquid oxygen, some 423 degrees below zero Fahrenheit at sea level. But the combined efficiency is around 450 seconds of specific impulse. NASA's Centaur and Saturn Projects will use the combination. Liquid hydrogen will also be used in the nuclear rockets of Project Rover. It will be heated by passing through the reactor and then ejected through the engine nozzle as a high-energy gas.

Basic booster engines of the Saturn Project will have a combined rating of one-and-a-half million pounds of thrust. They actually will be a cluster of eight rocket engines. A single-barreled engine, designated the F-1, to give the same powerful thrust is now in the works at North American Aviation. Atop these huge engines can be placed a modified Titan II ICBM and a nuclear top stage, to make interplanetary exploration feasible.

Still more important, a handful of America's leading Space Age manufacturers have been engaged in serious developmental work on electric rocket engines. These will not operate within the earth's atmosphere, since they require a vacuum. Yet their specific impulse is so tremendous that they could be used for manned interplanetary voyages *under power all the way.* This would cut travel-time down considerably, since the space crew could navigate their way to Mars, for example, on a direct route, rather than coast with power off along a ballistic trajectory to intercept the planet at a certain point of its orbit. The estimated time for a round trip between earth and Mars on the ballistic route is over three years. Powered by electric engines, the space ship could make the round trip in a year. Diagrams illustrating such engines are included in this chapter.

Among the big Space Age manufacturers involved in developmental work of advanced rocket engines, both nuclear and electric, are United Aircraft Corporation's Research Laboratories, Lockheed's Missiles and Space Division, two departments of the General Electric Company and several divisions of The Martin Company. These companies, among a few others— through building a storehouse of scientific and engineering brainpower plus having the imagination and courage to use it with vigor—have assured their future in the highly competitive Age of Space. Pioneer of the group is Martin. Long before the

Soviets made spaceflight a respectable word by launching Sputnik I, The Martin Company was investigating the force of gravity as a possible means of propulsion. They did this at their own expense, under no special contract. Now they have been joined by a few others.

Within the next five years to a decade, there should be orbiting laboratories in space, manned by scientists. Then the exotic propulsion systems might quickly become reality. Then, too, it might eventually become possible to achieve the proposals of Dr. Fritz Zwicky, one of the world's foremost astrophysicists and pro-

Powered by nuclear source shielded at end of a boom and sealed and pressurized to maintain its own atmosphere, this orbital lab should support 10 men for 6 months, say Lockheed designers.

Painting by Montgomery, from
Lockheed Missiles and Space Division

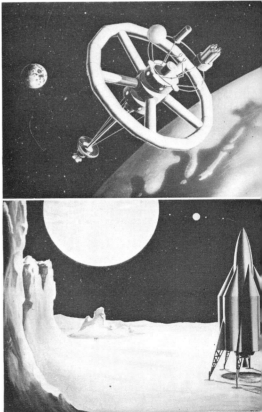

Painting by R. Simpson, from Douglas Aircraft

Douglas Aircraft engineers predict economically feasible voyages to Jupiter after nuclear thrust space ship engines are perfected. Above is artist's view of landing on largest of Jupiter's 12 moons.

pulsion authorities. Dr. Zwicky, now at CalTech and Mt. Wilson-Palomar Observatories, proposes the real possibility of rearranging the solar system in order to colonize planets such as Mars and Jupiter. Using man's advancing knowledge of the atomic nucleus and thermonuclear energy, Dr. Zwicky feels that water and a heavier atmosphere can be provided Mars by dislocating from orbit one of Jupiter's larger moons, to send it crashing onto the Martian surface—where its frozen atmosphere could be melted and held by the gravity of Mars. Equally he feels that Jupiter itself, giant planet of the solar system, could be increased in mass, given a breathable atmosphere and towed to an orbit closer to the sun to make it habitable.

If these appear to be wild ideas, a quotation from another propulsion expert should dispel the thought. He is Don L. Walter, Vice-President of the Power Systems Group at The Marquardt Corporation. Speaking before the Los Angeles Section of the Institute of Aerospace Sciences last summer, he said: "If we project history into the future, we must conclude that enormous progress will continue to be made. Propulsion devices such as ion, plasma, and even photon propulsion are presently envisioned. . . Perhaps, some day, people will look back upon statements that 'you can't travel faster than light' with the same sort of amusement that is occasioned now by reading the learned pronouncements on the futility of cracking the sound barrier.

"There is one thing I know . . . it is dangerous to say 'it can't be done.' And I highly suspect that around the next corner is an open road."

The italicized emphasis is his own. ●

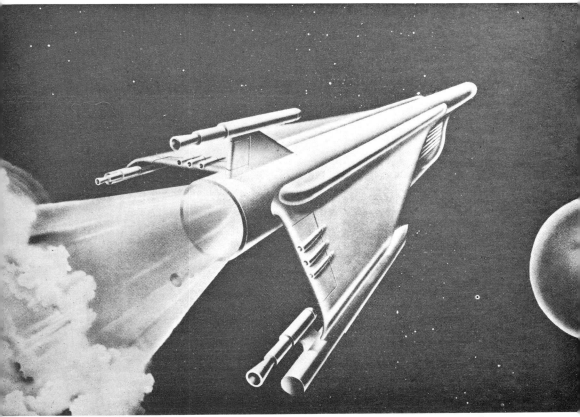

Engineering projection from The Martin Company

This nuclear-powered space ship has differences in design-concept from DYNA-SOAR glider, but both have one thing in common: aerodynamic lift surfaces of delta shape. This will enable crew to control landings on planets with atmospheres, including earth. DYNA-SOAR is test bed for space ships like these, will also give pilots know-how on landings. Space ship conceived by Martin-Denver engineers.

All illustrations in this chapter are from The Martin Company, except the large astrophoto by Harvey Hepworth; Mars landing directly below was painted for Martin by Artist Paul Rossi; other drawings were made by Kersivill of the Denver Division

Against a backdrop of the Great Spiral Nebula in Constellation of Andromeda, men set foot on one of the two moons of Mars. Shining behind them against their space ship and space suits is the Red Planet. Far in intergalactic space lies Andromeda Galaxy, a sister universe to the Milky Way. Some day, it may be necessary for man to reach that galaxy. Scientists are already thinking about such a trip.

homesteading the STARS

Machines that think for themselves, containing
whole civilizations, might be Columbuses of space.

"IF Life has purpose and changes in Life (mutations) are in accord
with a Plan, then it would not be surprising if the first signs of development of Macro Life were already in evidence, as in fact they are."

This tantalizing statement—lifted out of context, it is also enigmatic—
was made by a Space Age engineer speaking by invitation at the Annual
Meeting of The Institute of Navigation, U. S. Air Force Academy, in June
1960. His long and detailed lecture was entitled "Extraterrestrial
Colonies." It not only explained the meaning behind his coined expression, Macro Life, which literally translates into "life on a cosmic scale,"
but it presented some remarkable proposals for making the expression
a reality.

The engineer who presented these proposals was Dandridge M. Cole
of the Advanced Planning Department at The Martin Company's Denver,
Colorado, Division. The Division, as has been mentioned elsewhere in
this book, produces the Titan ICBM, around which many plans for
future space exploration are being formulated.

Mr. Cole conceives Macro Life in terms of gigantic cosmic "creatures," with human beings making up a portion of their multithousand
"cells." Other cells, creating each creature's brain and memory, would be
all the books in the Congressional Library recorded on microfilm and an
array of electronic computing systems. The heart of each would be a

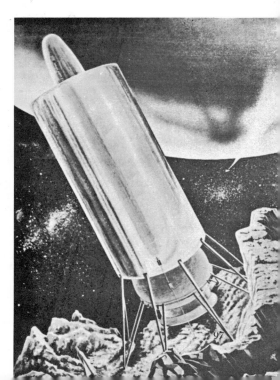

Example of Macro Life Creature
is seen at right. It, too, has just
landed on one of small moons of
Mars, yet compare it to space
pilots opposite. They and their
space ship may appear to be so
much more natty, but in reality
they represent a primitive first
step into space. The monster
here weighs about 75,000 tons,
is 1,000 ft. long, 420 ft. in outside diameter, has payload of
25,000 tons and can accom-
modate 10,000 passengers—a
civilization of men and women
as well as their children. This
is a ship to colonize the stars.

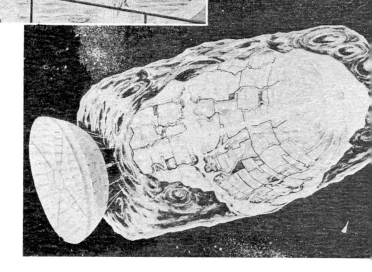

At left is Lunar Pleasure Dome, designed for those colonizers of the moon who may want to relax occasionally in the earth-style to which they have become unavoidably accustomed. Full sunlight, of course, would make it more than hot enough for swimming. Transparent plastic dome walls would have to contain special substance to deflect heat, stop water from boiling.

At right is concept of using hollowed-out minor planet as body of Macro Creature. It is Asteroid Colony I and travels in minor planet orbital belt between Mars and Jupiter, making use of nuclear energy inherent in metals and rock that comprise asteroids to obtain power. Note also the solar "dish" or mirror to gather additional energy from sun.

solar or nuclear power plant. Its muscles would be motors, gyros and servomechanisms. Its eyes would be electronic sensing devices. Its respiratory system would be self-sustaining through a hermetically closed gas process that would supply breathable oxygen and life-sustaining food from waste products and toxic gases exhaled. Its skin would be indestructible, as would be its skeleton, "far exceeding in toughness that of any animal and capable of withstanding the stresses of any environment except that of close proximity to the sun."

"This brute of the Space Age," says Mr. Cole, would be "theoretically immortal (barring accidents), both individually and collectively. It will be capable of growth, motion, reproduction, self repair, and vigorous and adequate response to almost any conceivable type of external stimulus.

"Macro Life individuals," he continues, "in some forms will be capable of high-speed motion through air, water, or vacuum. Individuals will be of enormous size compared to other life forms, with the smallest exceeding some 400 feet in diameter. Minimum weight will be on the order of five thousand tons, with 50 thousand tons being more typical of mature individuals. There will be no upper limit on the size and weight to which one of these immortal creatures might grow. Its sensory apparatus will far exceed in versatility and capability that of any individual or collection of animals or men. Its knowledge will equal that of the entire human race."

In other words, a Macro Life Creature would be a machine that thinks for itself, learns quickly from its mistakes and acts firmly on its own decisions, which are uncomplicated by emotional conflicts. Such a

machine would make possible the safe exploration of space, with its many yet unpredictable dangers, or the surfaces of alien worlds, with their unforseen hazards.

At Martin's Denver Division, Dr. John Fink, a psychologist, told me the possibilities of such machines. He calls them "SBS," or Synthetic Behavior Systems. Since they would be impervious to extremes of temperature, violent radiations and many unsuspected pitfalls that lie ready to trap or destroy man as he ventures forth in the Universe, such machines could analyze and map the danger areas as well as the particular kinds of dangers anywhere in space, on a hostile planet or on the moon.

In effect, Macro Life Space Creatures are highly mechanized and compressed civilizations in which human beings could exist among the stars. The illustrations on these pages depict a few forms the creatures

might take. They are designed so that men could not only live and learn happily inside them, but they would protect and nourish the future of mankind. The human population on earth increases by double the number every half-century. Natural resources, including energy, are gradually being depleted. Some day, man may be forced to leave this rich, green planet. When that day comes, he had better be ready to discover other, equally flourishing planets—or at the very least, be prepared to colonize less verdant worlds.

The development of mighty missiles is making journeys of space exploration possible. The far-sighted vision of Martin-Denver's scientists and engineers, along with the scientists and engineers of a number of other leading missile manufacturers, are already thinking of the far future and preparing for it. •

STRATEGIC

WEAPONS

Strategic targets demand a variety of devastating weapons to discourage enemy attack.

IN terms of discouraging an enemy from ever seriously thinking of waging war, the Strategic Air Command of the U. S. Air Force is a mighty deterrent. Proof of this is the bombastic accusations hurled at SAC by Communists around the world and particularly those in the Kremlin. The commander as well as the personnel of SAC are almost daily and loudly accused of being "warmongers." I have met many men of SAC and so I know personally that all of them—from their commander to the crew chiefs of bombers and missiles—are deeply sincere about the slogan by which they live. That slogan states flatly: "If we ever have to use our weapons in anger—they will have failed in their purpose."

Strategic warfare is combat on a global scale—as seen from the viewpoint of SAC. Strategic warfare as such is self-explained by the nature of strategic targets. These are targets which, if knocked out, would thoroughly paralyze an enemy's war-production facilities and weapon stockpiles, as well as destroy his will to resist. This would mean the planned destruction of his energy resources (oil fields and refineries, hydroelectric and nuclear power plants, gas compressor stations), his strategic industry (aircraft, missile, nuclear bomb and munitions factories, among others), his military training centers, launching pads and airfields, basic communications and transportation systems, test areas, steel mills and fabricating plants, shipping docks and submarine bases—all in his homeland.

Such a wide variety of targets requires a variety of weapons. This is why SAC has the Intercontinental Ballistic Missiles Atlas and Titan I, with Minuteman, Titan II coming. Atlas and Titan I are designed to destroy the heavyweight targets, Minuteman the medium-weight targets, and Titan II the extremely heavily fortified hardened targets. The target-variety also demands the use of global manned aircraft. The B-47 and B-52, both subsonic, can nevertheless accurately deliver nuclear and thermonuclear bombs of devastating power. The B-58, at double the speed of sound, can with in-flight refueling hustle to any point on earth and with equal accuracy deliver equal power on certain types of targets. This is why it has been named the "Hustler." It can be seen that both the manned aircraft and missiles are vitally and concurrently needed if an enemy is to be kept in place.

There are also strategic satellites. Some of these are called "passive" types by the Air Force. SAMOS is one of these. Its purpose is to reconnoiter on a strategic scale. Over the enemy homeland, it can photograph armament buildups and strategic targets. It acquired its name from the famous Greek island called Samos. Courier is another satellite that has strategic usefulness. It is a communications satellite that can receive, store and re-transmit by microwave radio—unhampered by weather conditions—either voice, television, teletype or code messages. It has built-in circuitry that rejects any radio signal not properly coded—so it cannot be jammed by an enemy. Since SAC's mission is global, a reliable worldwide unjammable communications system is a necessity. •

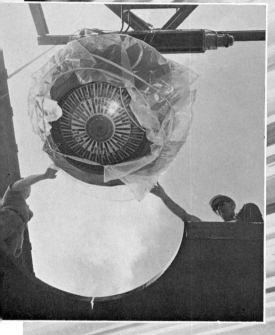

Large photo is Jupiter strategic missile, developed by Army for Air Force, which originally developed its engine. It is IRBM, or intermediate range ballistic type. Above is breakthrough in communications, the Courier satellite. It can maintain jam-proof global communications using human voice, TV, teletype or code.

Small photo: AF Ballistic Missile Div.; large: C. Rogers, AF Missile Test Center

Lockheed Missiles and Space Division

Above shows early flight test of Polaris strategic missile from ship's deck. Polaris is now operational in nuclear-powered subs, can be fired at targets from underwater, has a range of 1,200 miles.

At right is the mighty Titan I, designed to demolish heavyweight strategic targets. It can hurl big thermonuclear warheads across continents, over 6,000 miles. Titan II will have greater capability.

USAF Ballistic Missile Division

The Convair B-58 Hustler here being refueled in mid-air is a Mach 2 bomber that can carry big H-bombs to targets anywhere in the world. This piloted delta wing weapon is in inventory of Strategic Air Command and flew New York to Paris in 3 hours 20 minutes on May 26, 1961, 34th anniversary of Lindbergh's 33½-hour flight.

Photos: Minuteman, AF Ballistic Missile Div.; Titan, Martin-Cocoa; Atlas, McNearny, AF Missile Test Center

Above are shown from l. to r., Minuteman, Titan I and Atlas, all with strategic warheads. All are ballistic missiles with intercontinental range. Each has a special target-function and is necessary if SAC is to maintain its great deterrent power for protection of the Free World. These ICBMs are also making manned spaceflight possible—except for Minuteman, which is strictly a weapon-system, using solid fuel. However, it may add its bit to pure scientific research by supplying information on how solid rocket propellants may be used in future for manned ventures into space. At present, no solid-fuel rocket motor is powerful enough for purpose, nor can its burning rate be controlled sufficiently to hold back the changing rate of acceleration to a safe point for manned vehicles. Atlas and Titan both use controllable liquid fuels.

On facing page are shown Transit satellite and Thor strategic missile during launch of Transit, which also has strategic capability, since it is a navigational type—conceived by the Navy. Cooperation between Air Force and Navy is symbolized by USAF-SAC Thor being used as booster for Transit. Same booster was used to launch the Army-Defense Department Courier into orbit, thus making interservice cooperation more real than the much publicized (but largely mythical) rivalry. In both cases the Thor strategic missile used an Able-Star 2nd stage, which can be stopped and restarted in flight through space. The Able-Star stage is built by Aerojet-General, which also produces the mighty engines for Titan. SAC needs require not only great missiles and aircraft but also foolproof navigational and communications devices. Satellites are beginning to show great promise toward filling this extremely vital need.

Big photo by Don De-Fillips; smaller insets by Bud Janes; all from Air Force Missile Test Center

105

TACTICAL
WEAPONS

These weapon systems not only
defeat enemies on battlefields,
they also aid in space research.

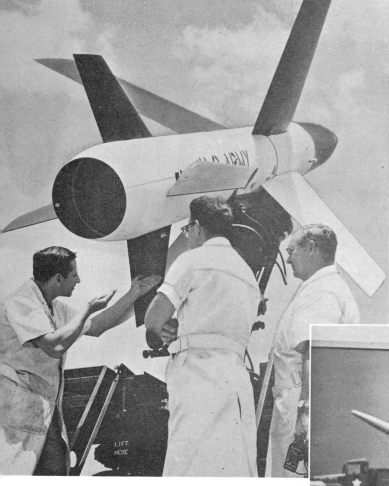

The Martin Company, Orlando Division

The Lacrosse missile on this page is lethal in its accuracy: during tests, it has struck a 2 x 4″ stake in ground 10 miles away as well as a 4 x 8″ target at 20 miles. It can carry warheads either nuclear or conventional to destroy pillboxes, other hardened emplacements in a single shot. Highly mobile, it is transportable on a standard 2½-ton Army truck, from which it is launched.

TACTICAL warfare may be compared to the shirtsleeved working "stiff," as opposed to strategic warfare, the executive body of the corporation. It is no less important because of this. If a hot war ever should start (and let's hope that the power of SAC will make this unfeasible for an enemy), the tactical units will be right in there—on or over the battlefield.

The extreme importance of modern tactical weapon systems cannot be understated. For although the Kremlin shouts boastfully of their huge arsenal of long-range ICBMs, the hard fact remains that the Reds are more familiar with land-army warfare than they are with strategic warfare. History bears this out—as do the juggernaut parades through Red Square each May Day and November 7th, the anniversary of the Bolshevik Revolution. I have seen one of these unbelievably massive parades myself—and the emphasis is on tactical warfare. I have watched newsreels of others—again, the emphasis is on weapons. So another great deterrent of the Free World against Communism is to have as varied an arsenal of ultramodern tactical weapons as possible. This means a much greater variety of weapons than is required even by strategic warfare—for the types of tactical targets range from foxholes and pillbox fortifications through missile emplacements, "abandoned" buildings, troop concentrations, food and other storage depots, bridges, railroads and rafts. Tactical targets must also be located and this demands reconnaissance, of which again there are many varieties. A wry new phrase has also come up, which demands tactical attention. This is "brush fire war." Korea was an example. Laos is another. All brush fire wars to date have been stimulated by the Reds, either directly or indirectly. Stamping out the brush fires of war, wherever they may start, is as important in preserving worldwide peace as is the threat of massive retaliation, exemplified by SAC.

But too often, the unglamorous aspects of tactical weapon systems cause them to escape public attention. Yet if the Marines had Lacrosse missiles during that period of World War II when they were fighting their way from island to island across the Pacific, they would have been able in comparative safety to rout the Japanese so well hidden in caves. If the Navy airmen had had Bullpup missiles, they could have knocked out bridges and antiaircraft emplacements without subjecting themselves to intense enemy fire. A Pershing missile, for example, with its selective range capability, would have saved many lives among United Nations troops in Korea— [Continued on page 110]

Lacrosse tactical missile just after launch during early tests at White Sands. Note telemetry antenna in nose to radio flight information. On operational models, this is no longer necessary.

Official U. S. Army Photo

Navy's newest tactical missile, the Tartar, is being tested here as antiaircraft weapon aboard the USS Norton Sound. Tartar can seek out and destroy aerial targets many miles away from ship.

General Dynamics Corporation, Convair Division

At right is the F-105B Thunderchief, supersonic fighter-bomber for use by Composite Strike Force of the Tactical Air Command. It can carry nuclear bombs or missiles and can perform reconnaissance missions also.

Official U. S. Air Force Photo

Below is F-100 Super Sabre, supersonic as well, in act of toss-bombing, a tactical technique developed at Air Proving Ground of USAF. F-100 dives toward target, tosses bomb from the wing, then pulls up sharply.

Air Proving Ground Center, Eglin AFB

Photo by author

Official U. S. Army Photo

Above is F-101 supersonic Voodoo, a versatile tactical fighter that can carry missile-bomb MB-1 Genie, a nuclear weapon capable of destroying a fleet of enemy fighters or other aircraft. It is mainly used in air defense. The Voodoo is one of few planes that can climb at supersonic speeds. It also has made reconnaissance photos at speeds beyond sound. A two-seat model is used by the Air Defense Command.

Highspeed Vulcan aerial cannon at r. has 6 barrels and can fire thousands of rounds per minute. It was developed by Army Ordnance for USAF and is used on some versions of Voodoo. Basic design was taken from Gatling Gun of Civil War fame. Still-photo here shows one of six barrels in action with tracers.

Official U. S. Army Photo

At left is Honest John, a free-flight artillery rocket of Army that can carry warheads of conventional or nuclear explosive impact. Its speed is supersonic. Range is 12 miles.

Official U. S. Navy Photo

At right are shown the Navy's Sparrow III air-to-air missiles being fired from an F3H-2 Demon aircraft. The Sparrow clings to its target, despite evasive action of enemy pilot, regardless of aiming errors.

and undoubtedly would have extinguished that brush fire war in a hurry. For the Army's Pershing, with extremely powerful nuclear warheads, can destroy hardened targets nearby or entire armies the distance of another battlefield away. A basic technique of tactical warfare is hit-and-run. All of the aforementioned missiles are highly mobile.

By this time, the reader should have a fairly good idea of the purpose of tactical weapon systems. Their function is to defeat an enemy on the battlefield—whether this be an area of 10 miles or 1,000 miles. This includes the destruction of his supply lines. It also includes the maintenance of our own lines of supply and transportation of troops plus equipment. The range covers everything from airlift by helicopter and airplane to tanks, missiles and machine guns. The variety is legion. Involved are the Tactical Air Command of the Air Force, the Naval Air Arm, the Army (of course) and the Marine Corps—to name only the fundamental participants.

It may, on the surface, appear amazing to the reader that the development of weapons strictly for use on the grim battlefield has also increased man's knowledge immeasurably in fields of pure space scientific research. The final chapter of this book, "Weapons for Science," explains why this is fact. ●

The Martin-built Matador tactical cruise-missile was first integrated missile-system based on new concept of weapon system design. It can carry nuclear warhead 600 miles, is deployed by TAC in Germany, Korea and Taiwan at the present.

Official US Air Force Photo

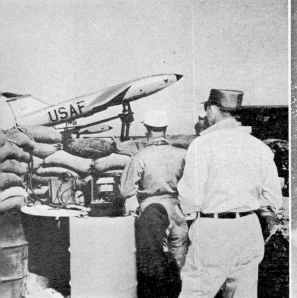

At right, Space Technology Labs., Inc., Official Photo

Satellite systems can help TAC as well as SAC. Here is shown SAMOS rising from a launch pad atop Atlas-Agena. SAMOS, for the Greek island of same name, was orbited successfully on Jan. 31, 1961, at the second attempt. As it passes over the world, it can take reconnaissance photos for both strategic and tactical purposes. At present, it is experimental.

On facing page are three views of Bullpup/GAM-83, said by the Navy to be world's most reliable missile. It is also the most versatile. Specifications were drawn by Navy and under inter-service agreement Air Force buys it for tactical use. Recent modification by USAF, GAM-83B, can carry nuclear warhead. Even more recently, the Marine Corps working with Martin-Orlando and Sikorsky perfected a way to launch Bullpup from helicopters. Missile is guided by pilot directly to targets he can see from a distance, thus assuring accuracy and safety from intense ground fire. Opposite photos show, from top down, helicopter firing of Bullpup; the Navy's FJ4 attack fighter, which carries five Bullpup air-to-ground missiles; and a GAM-83 being loaded into a USAF Super Sabre. Navy's code for missile is ASM-N-7. At right is Agena-Discoverer satellite being mated to a Thor missile for test-bed flight prior to SAMOS.

Photo above, from USAF Ballistic Missile Division; others. The Martin Co.: Baltimore, Orlando, Cocoa Divs.

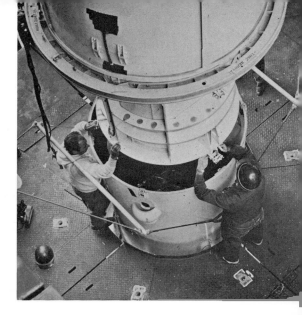

Directly above is MACE leaving its protective hard-site for an operational test flight. It was developed as a 2nd generation advanced tactical cruise-missile from the earlier Matador. MACE carries heavier nuclear payloads farther and faster. The "B" Model has a range of 1,200 miles and higher altitude. MACE has been deployed in Europe by TAC since 1959. At right is night-firing of Pershing, the Army's most versatile missile. It can deliver a huge nuclear "sock" on targets nearby or a battlefield away, because of a built-in selective range capability. Pershing has established records for successful continuous test-flights. It is a two-stage solid-fuel missile.

DEFENSE WEAPONS

Defense of America's homeland
is one of three integrated ways
to hold the enemy at bay.

U.S. AIR FORCE

AIR-DEFENSE is, of course, vitally and obviously necessary. In this case, we are talking about pure defense of our homeland against enemy attack—and not the tactical defense methods of the battlefield. The Continental United States was most favorably situated against enemy attack—until modern aerial weapons came on the scene. An enemy does not even need long-range ICBMs to penetrate the homeland of America. He can do it with long-range aircraft or missile-carrying submarines several hundreds of miles offshore—if these are not detected in time. He can, as the Kremlin certainly proves, find allies in nearby nations. Cuba, for instance, is within shooting distance of many important American target areas. From Cuba, a rocket as primitive as the German V-2 could be launched and create horrifying destruction in the United States. The Russians captured about 1,000 V-2s after World War II—many more than the U. S. forces obtained. This is only an example in passing. So whether or not the Red Army and Air Force have the wherewithal to attack the United States from bases in their own homeland is beside the point. There are other ways.

Fortunately, the United States has not been dozing. The total integrated aim of our Department of Defense has been to keep the enemy at bay in three ways: 1. By building a strategic power second to none—of such might that it would discourage an enemy from starting a war by any means. Yet if he were foolish enough to start one, that might would be available to paralyze his ability to fight. 2. By building the strongest and most versatile striking forces—so that if war tragically should occur, or if the enemy stimulated small wars without apparently participating to gain strength and weaken the Free World, he would find himself frustrated and demolished in action. 3. And finally, if he hoped to achieve a knockout blow against America by carrying forth a sneak massive attack upon the Continental United States, he would go down in defeat before that attack was barely started.

Point 3 is the subject of this chapter.

Defenses of our homeland must be as varied as the possible variety of an enemy's weapons. They must also be as automatic as possible for reasons of swift response and to prevent anyone from "pressing a button" in anger or fear. The enemy and his purpose must be identified beyond doubt. Otherwise, we might be guilty of starting a holocaust out of sheer, innocent uncertainty. Happily, there is little danger of this happening. There are too many checks and cross-checks, most of them electronic, all of them automatic.

Around the clock, the various groups and organizations of [*Continued on page* 118]

On facing page is Bomarc surface-to-air missile leaping toward sky to intercept an "enemy" aircraft. Actually, this was test of Bomarc-SAGE system. Enemy was radio-controlled drone far out over Atlantic Ocean off Cape Canaveral. SAGE control center, some 1,200 miles from Cape, automatically identified enemy and notified missile of target position, while launching it—all was done electronically, without touch of human hand.

Here is the interceptor version of supersonic Voodoo. Note two MB-1 Genie rockets beneath its belly. Either one of these could blast a squadron of enemy bombers out of the sky with nuclear blast.

On opposite page: Photo by C. Rogers, from Air Force Missile Test Center; Voodoo is Official USAF Photo

At far right is the lethal Nike-Hercules, surface-to-air guided missile that replaces Nike-Ajax to protect America's cities. It is commanded automatically by Missile Master, a control room of which is shown below. Missile Master electronically separates friendly aircraft from those of an enemy, then pinpoints positions and fires missiles to destroy enemy before it can drop bombs. BIRDiE, a mobile and compact version of the Missile Master has been developed to fit into van for hauling to out-of-way but strategic places. Directly at right is Nike-Zeus, an antimissile missile, being developed by Army to destroy possible enemy ICBMs. It would strike ICBM warhead high in atmosphere, demolishing it before it could do harm.

Nike-Hercules and Nike-Zeus, both Official U. S. Army Photos;
Missile Master photo from The Martin Company, Orlando Division

Directly above is a formation of F-102A Delta Daggers, approaching the sound-barrier on a supersonic practice mission. These interceptors, and the F-106 Delta Dagger, which was developed out of them, are fully operational with the North American Air Defense Command. They carry the Falcon missile, which transports a nuclear warhead. The Falcon's infra-red-sensitive nose guides it right into tailpipe of enemy jets. At right is Army's Hawk, a smaller surface-to-air guided missile designed specially to destroy enemy aircraft flying low to avoid radar detection. At bottom is Firebee drone, with F-102A practicing intercepts on it. Jet drone is a realistic target.

F-102A and Firebee drone photos by the author;
Hawk photo: Raytheon Manufacturing Company

On these two pages are aspects of MIDAS satellite. The initials mean Missile Defense-Alarm System. A test-model has been orbited by Atlas-Agena (facing page). At right is the Agena satellite modified with MIDAS instruments. Eventual purpose of MIDAS is to keep close watch on enemy strategic-missile ICBM launches. With sensitive infrared detection devices aboard, MIDAS can note any change in heat-balance of atmosphere, analyze amount of added heat-energy in terms of rocket-engine exhausts, determine the position of the missile and warn America's defenses in sufficient time to destroy it.

On this page: Photo from USAF Ballistic Missile Division; On opposite page: Photo by Fred Santomassino, from the Air Force Missile Test Center

the North American Air Defense Command are on the alert. These include the Army, Navy, Air Force and civilian groups. They include radar picket-aircraft and ships as well as "Texas Towers." Included are land-based warning centers across the United States and aircraft as well as missiles on-the-ready at key locations. Also active are BMEWS, the Ballisic Missile Early Warning System and SAGE, for Semi-Automatic Ground Environment, as well as Missile Master, a system that ties in with SAGE and automatically separates enemy from friendly aircraft to destroy the enemy craft automatically by launching ground-to-air missiles. All of these system are great achievements in electronics. All of them function with almost the speed of light.

Look at the photos in this chapter. Read the captions. And then decide if an enemy could strike a paralyzing blow against our homeland—as we can against his, if we were forced to do it. •

JETS behind the scenes

Step-by-slow-step, these largely unknown
experimental aircraft led the way
to America's superior airpower and space.

Except as noted, all photos in this chapter are from the files of the USAF Flight Test Center, Edwards AFB

Above is the YB-49, famous Flying Wing designed and built by Northrop. Only two were built, adapted from YB35s, original piston-powered Flying Wings. YB-49 jet flew cross-continent at 511.2 mph, proving feasibility of certain aspects of tailless aircraft, aiding other aircraft design.

At right is the D558-Phase I, a Douglas-built jet to investigate the transonic realm of flight. This is the no-man's-land between subsonic and supersonic speeds. Information gathered by this experimental airplane made possible D558-II, a rocket ship and first to fly at twice sonic speed.

SINCE October 14, 1947, news reports have often mentioned cryptic numbers when referring to record-breaking aircraft. On that date, a young Air Force experimental test pilot flew the first pure rocket-powered vehicle through the sound barrier and came back from what was then the fringe of space to tell about it. His name was "Chuck" Yeager. The "fringe of space" was about eight miles up. The rocket ship was the Bell-built XS-1.

Today, aircraft of the Air Force and Navy routinely fly at that altitude and some fly a few miles higher—with air-breathing turbojet engines, not rockets. But without Yeager's historic flight, this would not be possible. Supersonic aircraft, of which there are a number operational now, would have been impossible of achievement. Manned hypersonic aircraft, of which the X-15 is forerunner, would never have occurred to serious aeronautical engineers. And manned spaceflight would be nothing but a crackpot dream.

It is simple enough to talk about flight to the moon and planets. It is even easier to discuss sending a man into orbit around the earth. These are glamour ideas and come glib to the tongue—of those who have no knowledge of the sweat and stubbornness and dedication and faith that it has taken to reach the point where such events are probable and may be possible. When Yeager volunteered to take a rocket with wings through the sound barrier, there was no precedent for his flight. He had painstakingly flown the XS-1 week after week over the Mojave Desert, each time pushing it a little faster and climbing it a little higher. This was how he got the "feel" of the machine and could suggest modifications to the engineers: little changes here and there that made all the difference in the stability and controllability of the aircraft. Such human-supplied information over a long period was added to information radioed to ground tape recorders from instruments in the rocket ship, to deductions from photographs of others on the instrument panel. The result was a triumph of air technology.

The same process of painstaking testing conquered the so-called heat barrier and altitude barrier. The Bell X-2 rocket airplane was pioneer at these frontiers. "Pete" Everest, then a lt. colonel, flew the X-2 at 1,900 miles an hour. Iven Kincheloe, a captain, took it up to 126,000 feet—where the sky is black and stars shine while the curve of the earth below is brightly blue in sunlight. A friend of "Kinch's," Captain Mel Apt, took the rocket-powered

The XP-87 is shown here high above mountains surrounding Mojave Desert of California, where Flight Test Center of USAF is located at Edwards AFB. Base was named after Capt. Glen Edwards, who was killed in line of test-duty when YB-49 Flying Wing crashed. The Curtiss XP-87 was experimental jet pursuit plane, hence the XP designation. At middle of page is YP-59, the first American jet airplane. It was built by Bell Aircraft and pioneered way for modern supersonic fighters. The "Y" stands for "operational phase of testing." Below is XP-88, one of but two made. It was replaced as interceptor by F-89 ("F" for fighter), but led to design of supersonic F-101 Voodoo, also built by the McDonnell Aircraft Corp.

The two XP-90s here were only ones built by Lockheed. High fuel consumption and insufficient range killed them, but things learned made possible F-94C interceptor and F-104A, world's fastest fighter.

X-2 beyond 2,100 miles per hour—and died. Kinch himself was later tragically killed in an F-104 Starfighter—ironically, an operational Mach 2 fighter-interceptor that had been made possible only because of knowledge gained in high-speed, high-altitude experimental flights of the X-series aircraft.

In between, was the Navy's D-558 series of aircraft. The first of these Douglas-built airplanes was powered by a turbojet engine that, unlike a rocket, requires air for combustion of its fuel. But the D-558-I went transonic and was able to gather invaluable data on the flight regime that lies between a subsonic 600 miles per hour and the hard-packed "brick wall" of compressed air that is the front edge of the sound barrier. The D-558-II, using the same 4-barreled rocket engine as the XS-1, was the first airplane ever to fly at twice the speed of sound. Scotty Crossfield was at the controls.

Step-by-step new data was gathered as men flew higher and faster. Each new step added a few extra feet of altitude and miles-per-hour of speed. The more spectacular of these flights were news and so reached the public. But many of the experimental aircraft are still unknown and unsung—except to those who built and worked with them. They have remained behind the scenes for a number of reasons. All of them, at one time or another, were carefully guarded secrets. But each of them led toward better aircraft and gathered information that now makes manned flight in outer space a reasonable probability. They have also made possible the success of Project Mercury. They have raised the strategic, tactical and defensive airpower of the United States to pinnacles as yet not reached by any other nation. They are the "aero" portion of the concept "aerospace." The concept is expressed in a single word for good reason. Wings and other lifting surfaces are unnecessary in space, of course. But in order to reach space and return safely from it to earth—you need those wings. •

123

Above is XF-92, an experimental delta-winged fighter-interceptor. Out of many tests with it came data that made the F-102A supersonic interceptor a success. This led to F-106 as well, a Mach 2 delta. All three aircraft were produced by Convair. Information about delta wing shapes will help Project DYNA-SOAR.

Above is the XF-94, which finally was developed successfully into the F-94C Starfire, one of America's first operational, electronically controlled interceptors. Its pilot could be directed from ground to intercept enemy aircraft and destroy it automatically with rockets and guided missiles.

At left are the XRF-84F, reconnaissance version of the Thunderstreak, at top, and the XF-91, foreground. Swept wing Thunderflash became operational, was used late in Korean War. XF-91 was dropped after being used as a test-bed for combination rocket-turbojet engine effects. Both made by Republic.

125

Built by Consolidated Vultee Aircraft, the XB-46 was medium jet bomber designed for attack purposes. Only one model constructed, it was dropped in favor of B-47. Later, it was put to good use to develop and test pneumatic control systems in conditions of extremely low temperatures.

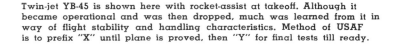

Twin-jet YB-45 is shown here with rocket-assist at takeoff. Although it became operational and was then dropped, much was learned from it in way of flight stability and handling characteristics. Method of USAF is to prefix "X" until plane is proved, then "Y" for final tests till ready.

During World War II, two of these XB-43s were built by Douglas Aircraft because of the rapid development of German jet bombers. Although test and development program took four years and three months, enough new aerodynamic information was obtained to supply basis for operational B-66 Destroyer.

Above is YB-60, by Convair. Note similarity of configuration with early version of B-52 (at right). Today, B-52 Stratofortress is a mainstay of the Strategic Air Command, yet it was developed out of the YB-60 test program. B-52 is a Boeing product, but economic competition does not invade field of our nation's defense posture. Both the manufacturers and military freely interchange new information for progress of all. The YB-60 has a higher number than the SAC bomber only because its general design specifications were conceived later. Actually, B-52 was built and tested later, profiting from data acquired by test flights of YB-60.

Shown at right is a B-47 Stratojet, although those familiar with nose-configuration of B-47s never would recognize this one. It was modified for special high-altitude research by National Advisory Committee for Aeronautics (NACA), now the National Aeronautics and Space Administration (NASA). Government space research organizations continually adapt for scientific use the standard operational aircraft of both past and present. At right, below, is the XB-51. Before this light jet bomber appeared, the YB-50 was developed out of B-29 Super Fortress. The B-50 was last of the piston-powered bombers, is used now as a test-bed for science research. The XB-51 proved the value of the J-47 turbojet engine. Only two were built for experiment by The Martin Company.

Photo above by the author

129

The German rocket-bombardment of London led in a straight line to use of missiles for scientific progress.

THE first rocket-powered weapon was the German V-2. It was used during the latter phase of World War II to bombard London. Ironically, it was derived from the peaceful scientific experiments of an American visionary physicist, Dr. Robert Goddard. Few serious engineers and scientists of his own land paid much attention to Dr. Goddard. Generally, he was ridiculed. Pamphlets describing his rocket experiments could at that time be purchased for less than 25 cents from the Smithsonian Institution. Again, few persons of note bothered to buy and read these —except the Germans. The first V-2 that exploded in London astonished and horrified the world. It was thoroughly unexpected. Traveling much faster than sound, nobody in London heard it coming. Fortunately, the Nazi Government had not developed this terrifying weapon until they were facing defeat beyond all doubt. After the war, about 150 V-2s were shipped to the United States to be used as research test beds. The White Sands Proving Ground of U. S. Army Ordnance was established as an inland missile range. Nearby, at Holloman Air Force Base, a Missile Development Center was founded. The Air Force and Army cooperated to discover everything they could about rockets. The V-2 had made a 180-degree turn and returned to America for scientific research.

Blue Scout photos and chart are from USAF Ballistic Missile Division

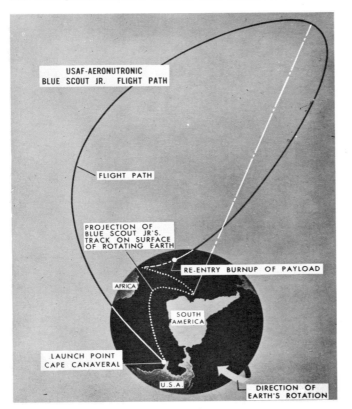

USAF-AERONUTRONIC BLUE SCOUT JR. FLIGHT PATH

FLIGHT PATH

PROJECTION OF BLUE SCOUT JR'S. TRACK ON SURFACE OF ROTATING EARTH

RE-ENTRY BURNUP OF PAYLOAD

AFRICA

SOUTH AMERICA

LAUNCH POINT CAPE CANAVERAL

U.S.A.

DIRECTION OF EARTH'S ROTATION

Official Army Ordnance Photo

Directly above is German V-2 rising from pad at the White Sands Proving Ground during late 1940s. About 150 V-2s were "liberated" after World War II, shipped to New Mexico for peaceful experimental flight tests. Across these two pages are photos of HETS Blue Scout, newest pure research rocket of USAF. Chart shows flight path of 3-stage Junior model. Senior model, flown by NASA, has most powerful solid-fuel engines in Free World, about 100,000 lbs. thrust. HETS means Hyper-Environmental Test System. Air Force has "Blue Suit" Program to train own crews.

At right is Viking Research Rocket No. 9, product of The Martin Co. and America's first originally designed heavyweight for pure space research. Vikings made first clear photos of the earth.

Earlier version of the V-2 was this A-3B below. V-2 was originally designated A-4 by Germans. Model shown here was used by General Electric scientists as part of program to develop Bumper.

Special Defense Products Dept., GE Co.

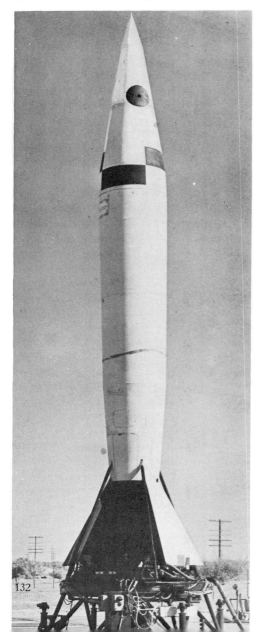

Naval Research Laboratory

The Aerobee, solid booster end-foremost, is seen below being raised to vertical position in its launcher at Holloman AFB. Made by Aerojet-General Corp., code-designation then was MX-1011.

USAF Missile Development Center

Above is HTV (Hypersonic Test Vehicle), an early rocket for researching atmospheric friction-heating of ballistic missile nose cones. HTV flew, to mere 500 ft. but at Mach 7, or 7 times sound-speed.

Not much later, the Naval Bureau of Aeronautics and Research Laboratory devised the specifications for two rockets planned for pure scientific research in the earth's upper atmosphere. These were the Viking, built by the Glenn L. Martin Company (now simply The Martin Company), and the Aerobee, built by the Aerojet-General Corporation (formerly the Aerojet Engineering Corporation). These two companies today cooperate on production of the mightiest rocket of them all— Titan. Aerojet-General designed and builds the engines. Martin-Denver, as prime contractor and systems manager, puts Titan together and tests it both on the ground and in the sky.

Technical information and experience gained from Viking and Aerobee, in no small way, made Titan possible.

The Aerobee was finally purchased by the Air Force and modified for ever more advanced high-altitude probes. Now the Air Force, Navy *and* Army were cooperating. Without such cooperation, American rocketry could not be where it is today— at the forefront of world technology. "In-

Deacon rocket shown below is being lifted to the vertical launch position aboard USS Staten Island. It's then carried by stratospheric balloon to a high altitude for firing. System name: "Rockoon."

Above is Bumper No. 5, as launched from White Sands in Feb. 1949. The V-2 1st stage boosted little WAC-Corporal 252 miles high. Bumper was the 1st 2-stage missile to successfully fly. It led way to all modern multistage rocket programs.

Below is 2-stage rocket used by NASA to test ejection of balloon satellites and their inflation mechanism. Result of such tests was "Echo," the 100-ft. diam. satellite still orbiting as a new visible "star." Test-rocket was clever adaptation of standard Army rockets.

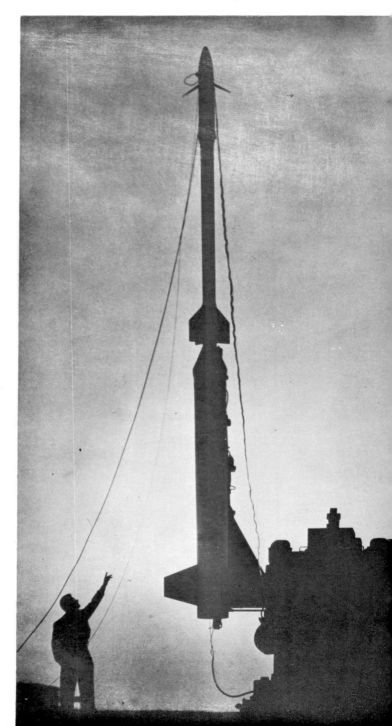

Below is early test vehicle at Wallops Island, used to propel aerodynamic shapes to five times the speed of sound. Shape shown is of hypersonic glider, which led to Project DYNA-SOAR. Rocket and launcher are Navy's antiaircraft Terrier.

National Aeronautics & Space Administration Photos

Above 3-stage rocket was made from weapons also: 1st stage is Honest John artillery rocket and 2nd stage is Nike-Ajax booster, both Army. While 3rd stage was NASA's own, to probe heat transfer.

At left is 5-stage rocket, a remarkable achievement at low cost. It combined standard rockets to research speeds beyond 10 times sound. Honest John, 2 Nikes, a Recruit and T-55 were stages.

ter-service rivalries" so often mentioned by politicians and the press are simply another myth of the Space Age. The 3-service cooperation continues today at Cape Cañaveral, Point Arguello and Edwards Air Force Base.

The mighty Titan is a 2-stage missile. The rocket engine of its second stage ignites after the first stage has boosted it into the ultra-thin-air regions above the stratosphere and sends it on to accelerate from a speed of about 5,000 miles an hour. Titan finally reaches speeds beyond 15,000 miles an hour at the fringe of space and

Photo by Wyman, from AF Missile Test Center

Above is the Jupiter strategic medium-range missile. It was developed by Army's Ballistic Missile Agency and turned over to the Air Force. Adaptations are used in scientific research.

Photo by Vestby, from AF Missile Test Center

Juno II, above, is one modification of Jupiter missile. It successfully flung America's first solar satellite past the moon and into an elongated orbit around the sun that crosses Mars' orbit.

Lockheed Missiles and Space Division

At left is Lockheed's X-17, a 3-stage solid-fuel rocket that helped develop ICBM re-entry nose cones. X-17 shown here was adapted for Project Argus, a world-shaking scientific accomplishment.

arcs across continents. But in 1949, when the V-2 was mated to a small WAC-Corporal rocket, it was an unprecedented success that a 2-stage missile could boost its tiny second stage 252 miles high at speeds around 5,000 miles an hour. The project, supervised by the General Electric Company, was called "Bumper" for obvious reasons. It was the beginning of multistage rockets.

Simultaneously with the Bumper-WAC, other rockets and missiles were rapidly being developed. The Army's Honest John, Corporal and Nike-Ajax; the Navy's Terrier and Regulus; the Air Force's XS-1 and Navaho; were all in the works. When they became available, events occurred swiftly: the sound barrier was broken in level flight with the XS-1 rocket-powered aircraft, piloted by (then) Captain "Chuck"

Photo by Rogers, from Air Force Missile Test Center

Note the big rocket booster on which sits the Navaho Missile test vehicle. Navaho was dropped by USAF, but not before booster engine was perfected. In modified form, it now powers both Jupiter and Thor missiles.

Inset photo is SAMOS satellite being prepared for launch by Atlas-Agena rocket. To avoid contamination, which would destroy test purposes, it was kept in a dust-free, surgically clean room.

USAF Ballistic Missile Division

Photo by Don De Fillips, from Air Force Missile Test Center

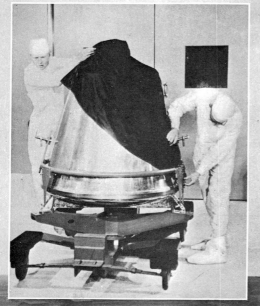

Large photo shows launch of 3-stage Thor-Able rocket carrying the Tiros weather-scanning satellite. During its active life, the 270-lb. Tiros telecast some 25,000 photos of clouds and storms.

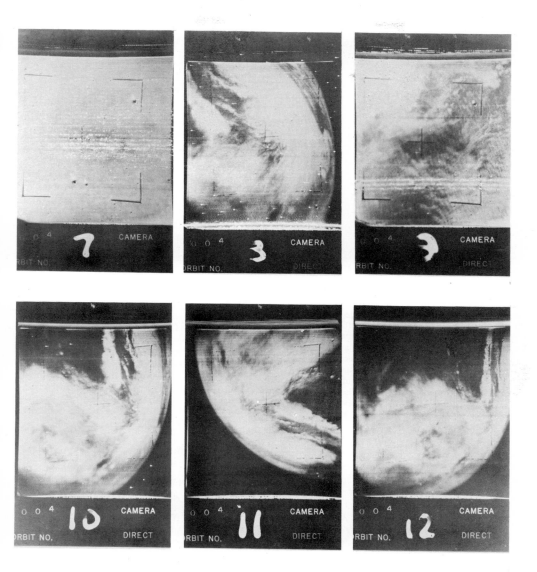

Photos of Planet Earth taken in outer space by close-up and wide angle television cameras in the TIROS weather reconnaissance satellite. The written numbers indicate orbits 7 through 12 of the satellite. National Aeronautics and Space Administration.

Photo by Gene Adams, Lockheed Missiles and Space Division; chart from same Division

Maj. General Osmond J. Ritland (left) and Colonel Preston Newton sit at control console of Satellite Test Center, Sunnyvale, Calif. Colonel Newton directs the Center, which is part of Ballistic Missile Division, commanded by General Ritland. Center directs tracking and control stations from New England to Alaska and Pacific islands ranging from Hawaii southward, including tracking vessels and aircraft. Recovery of capsules from the Discoverer satellites is main task. These are testbeds for SAMOS, MIDAS and other advanced satellite systems. Chart shows how capsules are ejected.

Yeager; amazing new knowledge was acquired about hypersonic flight regimes by the National Advisory Committee for Aeronautics (NACA) at their Wallops Island Proving Ground off the Virginia coast; and the first strategic missiles were made possible. It is significant that NACA finally developed into the National Aeronautics and Space Administration (NASA). In a sense, they pulled themselves up by their bootstraps. Their

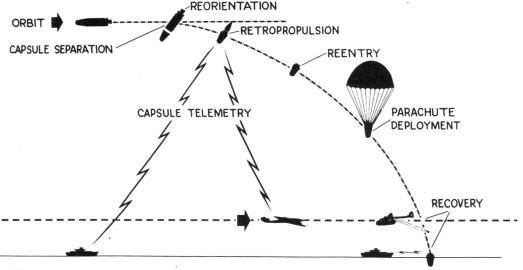

ORBIT

CAPSULE SEPARATION

REORIENTATION

RETROPROPULSION

REENTRY

CAPSULE TELEMETRY

PARACHUTE DEPLOYMENT

RECOVERY

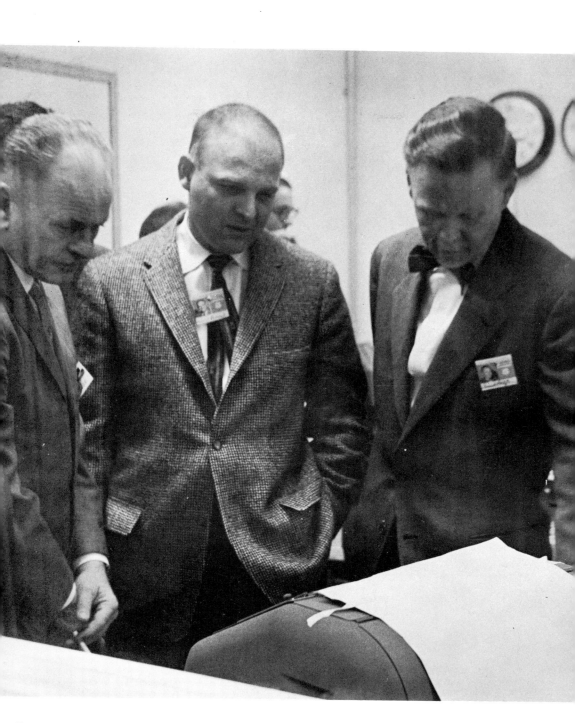

Tenseness prior to Pacific Missile Range launch is caught here by the candid camera at the Air Force Space Systems Division. Maj. General Osmond J. Ritland, Commander, Maurice Cristadoro, project chief on ATLAS ICBM Program, and Colonel Albert Wetzel, project chief on the TITAN ICBM Program (left to right) read teletype messages from nearby Vandenburg Air Force Base.

Air Force Space Systems Division

Photo at right by Ragnar Petersen,
Lockheed Missiles and Space Division

Above is C-119 Flying Boxcar in act of snatching
Discoverer satellite's capsule out of the air.
Pilot has been directed to area and ordered to
make snatch by controllers at Satellite Test
Center some 2,500 miles away. Quoting Colonel
Newton, "Ejecting capsules and snatching them in
mid-air has become routine." At right, foreground,
General Schriever studies capsule with scientist.

Photo by McNearny & Crowe,
Air Force Missile Test Center

Reaction Motors—Thiokol

At left, MX-774 missile
rises from White Sands
pad. Note extreme simi-
larity to the German V-2
on page 131, from which
it was developed with
some improvements. It
served as test bed for Atlas
(shown at right), the earli-
est ICBM. From such small
beginnings grew the whole
of America's missilery—
which is second to none in
the world today. From
cruder beginnings of Dr.
Robert Goddard, pioneer
physicist who made the
rocket work as a practical
vehicle, the Germans took
their plans for the V-2. Its
engine is almost identical
with the liquid-fuel rockets
that the American scientist
was launching in the late
1930s from his private
proving ground in the
desert at Roswell, N. M.

achievements at Wallops Island were based on skill, ingenuity and persistence. One of these achievements was the first successful 5-stage rocket. They made it up from "borrowed" parts: Nike-Ajax boosters and Honest John rockets—both weapons of war. Other multistage rockets they put together from Terriers and Corporals—again, weapons of war. Out of their program came the 3-stage X-17, which made possible Intercontinental Ballistic Missiles by developing re-entry nose cones. The Navaho intercontinental cruise missile was abandoned, but development of its rocket-booster engines made Thor and Jupiter possible. And these, in turn, have boosted into outer space many, many scientific probes to revolutionize man's concept of the Universe. ●

But first of America's big rockets that worked like a Swiss watch was the Viking. Just as the MX-774 laid the basis of Atlas, so Viking led the way to Titan, an advanced ICBM of greater power.

Mighty thrust of rocket engine propels Martin-built U. S. Army PERSHING ballistic missile skyward from Cape Cañaveral, Florida. PERSHING, POLARIS and MINUTEMAN (all solid-fuel missiles) are providing engineers with knowledge of behavior and controllability of solid rocket propellants that should lead toward new types of space-research engines.

143

Twilight before dawn at Cape Cañaveral, Florida, reveals a TITAN ICBM in its gantry servicing tower as the count down progresses toward another test flight of America's mightiest missile.

Air Force Space Systems Division